CONTENTS

KT-116-937

INTRODUCTION

STRUCTURE

This book is designed for pupils of all abilities to learn key ideas 1–5 of the Scottish Standard Grade Geography syllabus and to develop the gathering and processing techniques prescribed in the syllabus. The book is divided into fourteen units and each unit is divided into several sections:

1 all pupils read the **Core text**
2 all pupils answer the **Core questions**.
Pupils then choose to
3 answer the **Foundation questions**
   or
4 answer the **General questions**
   or
5 read the **Extension text** and answer the **Extension questions** and the **Credit questions**.

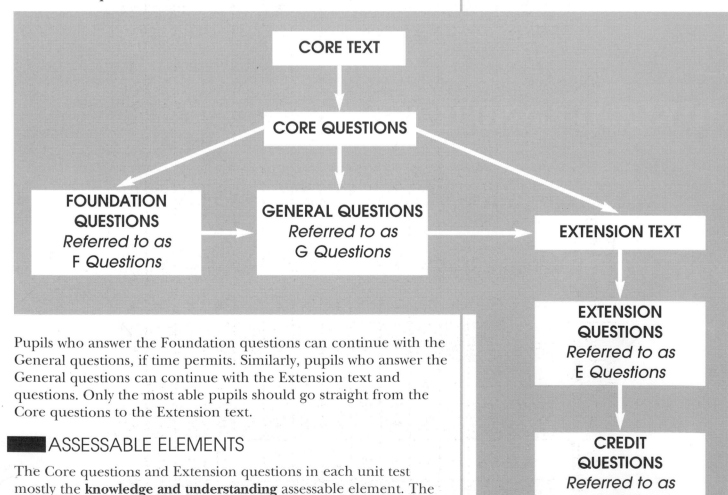

CORE TEXT

CORE QUESTIONS

FOUNDATION QUESTIONS
Referred to as
F *Questions*

GENERAL QUESTIONS
Referred to as
G *Questions*

EXTENSION TEXT

EXTENSION QUESTIONS
Referred to as
E *Questions*

CREDIT QUESTIONS
Referred to as
C *Questions*

Pupils who answer the Foundation questions can continue with the General questions, if time permits. Similarly, pupils who answer the General questions can continue with the Extension text and questions. Only the most able pupils should go straight from the Core questions to the Extension text.

ASSESSABLE ELEMENTS

The Core questions and Extension questions in each unit test mostly the **knowledge and understanding** assessable element. The Foundation, General and Credit questions test mostly the **enquiry skills** assessable element.

The PHYSICAL ENVIRONMENT

CALVIN CLARKE

Hodder & Stoughton
A MEMBER OF THE HODDER HEADLINE GROUP

STANDARD
GRADE
GEOGRAPHY

ACKNOWLEDGEMENTS

The publishers would like to thank the following individuals, institutions and companies for permission to reproduce photographs in this book. Every effort has been made to trace ownership of copyright. The publishers would be happy to make arrangements with any copyright holder whom it has not been possible to contact:

Bryan & Cherry Alexander Photography (78 top and bottom); J. Allan Cash Ltd (34, 47, 63, 64 top left, 65 top, 103, 106, 112 top, 113); Heather Angel/Biofotos (59); Calvin Clarke (16, 94); Corbis (68, 72, 75); Pauline & David Davies (42, 116, 121); Dundee Satellite Receiving Station/The National Meteorological Picture Library (38); Leslie Garland Picture Library/Philip Nixon (96 bottom); GSF Picture Library (119 top); Hutchison/Robert Francis (107), /Michael Harvey (55), /Chris Parker (64 top right), /P. Edward Parker (45), /Bernard Régent (71); Life File/Caroline Field (112 bottom), /David Heath (56), /Barry Mayes (117), /Lionel Moss (119 bottom); John Noble Wilderness Photographic Library (96 top); Tony Waltham Geophotos (65 bottom, 115 top and bottom)

Orders: please contact Bookpoint Ltd, 39 Milton Park, Abingdon, Oxon OX14 4TD. Telephone: (44) 01235 400414, Fax: (44) 01235 400454. Lines are open from 9.00–6.00, Monday to Saturday, with a 24 hour message answering service. Email address: orders@bookpoint.co.uk

British Library Cataloguing in Publication Data
A catalogue record for this title is available from The British Library

ISBN 0 340 69088 7

First published 1998
Impression number   10 9 8 7 6 5 4 3 2 1
Year   2004 2003 2002 2001 2000 1999 1998

Cover photo from Telegraph Colour Library.

Illustrations by Chartwell Illustrators.

Typeset by Fakenham Photosetting Limited, Fakenham, Norfolk NR21 8NL.
Printed in Great Britain for Hodder & Stoughton Education, a division of Hodder Headline Plc, 338 Euston Road, London NW1 3BH by Redwood Books Ltd, Trowbridge, Wiltshire.

Unit	Key Ideas	Knowledge Understanding (F/G levels) a	b	c	Knowledge Understanding (G/C levels) a	b	c	Enquiry Skills (F level) a	b	c	d	e	Enquiry Skills (G level) a	b	c	d	e	Enquiry Skills (C level) a	b	c	d	e
1	2			✓			✓				✓	✓				✓	✓				✓	✓
2	2	✓	✓	✓	✓		✓	✓	✓	✓			✓	✓	✓			✓	✓	✓		
3	2	✓	✓		✓			✓	✓	✓			✓	✓	✓			✓	✓			
4	2	✓	✓			✓		✓	✓	✓			✓	✓	✓			✓	✓			
5	4	✓				✓		✓	✓	✓			✓	✓	✓			✓	✓	✓		
6	3	✓		✓			✓					✓					✓					✓
7	3/4	✓	✓	✓	✓		✓	✓	✓	✓			✓	✓	✓			✓	✓	✓		
8	3/4	✓	✓	✓	✓			✓	✓	✓			✓	✓	✓			✓	✓			
9	3/4	✓	✓	✓	✓	✓		✓	✓	✓			✓	✓				✓	✓			
10	1	✓					✓				✓	✓				✓	✓				✓	✓
11	1/4	✓	✓		✓		✓	✓	✓				✓		✓			✓	✓			
12	1/4/5	✓	✓		✓	✓		✓	✓	✓			✓	✓	✓			✓		✓		
13	1/4	✓	✓		✓	✓		✓	✓	✓			✓	✓				✓	✓	✓		
14		✓	✓	✓	✓		✓	✓	✓	✓			✓	✓				✓		✓		

UNIT ① Skills in Weather Studies

Core Text

1A INTRODUCTION TO WEATHER STUDIES

Geography studies **landscapes**. In particular, it studies the ways in which the **physical landscape** affects people and their activities (the **human landscape**). It is therefore important in geography to study the weather because (a) it affects the physical landscape (for example the vegetation that grows, the number of rivers, the shape of the hills) and (b) it affects the human landscape (for example what and how people farm, the types of housing).

For the Standard Grade examination, you need to know and understanding the following:
1 the elements of the weather
2 the weather associated with fronts, depressions and anticyclones
3 the methods used to forecast the weather
4 the effects of weather on people

You also need to develop the following enquiry skills:
1 how and where to gather weather information, by measuring and observing the weather elements and recording them on weather maps
2 how to process weather information, by using line graphs and bar graphs
3 how to analyse weather information.

The rest of this unit deals with ways of gathering and processing weather information.

1B GATHERING INFORMATION

There are many different ways of finding out about the weather. These ways are called **gathering techniques**. For example, to investigate the topics studied for Standard Grade some of the techniques that can be used are listed in Figure 1.1:

Figure 1.1	
Topic studied	**Gathering technique**
Weather elements	**Observing and recording** cloud cover, cloud type, windspeed, visibility **Measuring** temperature, precipitation, windspeed, sunshine, wind direction, air pressure **Extracting information** from satellite photos, radar images
Weather maps and weather forecasts	**Extracting information** from TV, newspapers, Meteorological Office
Effects of weather on people	**Interviewing** people affected by the weather

1C PROCESSING INFORMATION

Once you have gathered all the information you need, it has to be analysed. To do this, you first need to arrange it into a form that is easier to use. For example, much of the information you find out about the weather can be shown on maps, graphs, tables and diagrams. When you change your 'raw' findings into a more useful form, you are using 'processing techniques.' Some useful processing techniques in weather studies are now described in detail.

1D DRAWING A LINE GRAPH

A line graph is used to show how an amount changes over time or distance. You can draw a line graph in the following way:
- draw x (horizontal) and y (vertical) axes in pencil
- plot time or distance on the x axis, for example in Figure 1.2 the x axis shows 'days in August 1997'
- the y axis shows show an amount, for example in Figure 1.2 the y axis shows the temperature in degrees Celsius
- find the highest and lowest values required on the x and y axis and then choose a suitable scale for each axis
- label the axes in ink, including the units
- plot each point carefully, in pencil, with a small cross or dot
- join the points with a pencil line
- once you have checked your graph, go over the pencil line in ink
- write a title for the graph.

1E DRAWING A MULTIPLE LINE GRAPH

A multiple line graph is one in which two or more line graphs are shown on the same diagram (see Figure 1.3). Multiple line graphs are used to compare changes in two or more measurements over time or distance. You can draw a multiple line graph in the following way:
- draw x and y axes
- select a suitable scale for each axis
- if the graphs have different units (for example a graph of the **number** of farmworkers and a graph of farmworkers' **wages**),

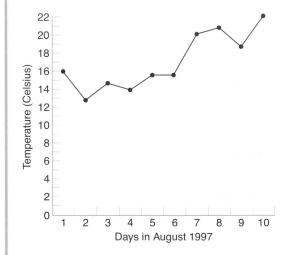

Figure 1.2 Mean temperatures in Glasgow, August 1997

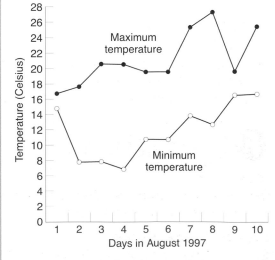

Figure 1.3 Maximum and minimum temperatures in Glasgow, 1–10 August 1997

another *y* axis can be drawn up the right-hand side of the graph and an appropriate scale used for the second unit
- draw each line graph separately
- label each graph line clearly
- give the graph a title.

1F DRAWING A BAR GRAPH

A bar graph is used when there is only one amount. This graph compares the amount of several different items. You can draw a bar graph in the following way:
- draw *x* (horizontal) and *y* (vertical) axes in pencil
- use the *y* axis to show the information that is an amount, for example in Figure 1.4 the *y* axis shows the **amount** of sunshine
- find the highest value required on the *y* axis and work out a suitable scale
- find the number of 'bars' you need to draw and then decide how wide each bar should be
- label the axes in ink, including the units
- draw each bar carefully in pencil
- once you have checked your graph, go over the pencil lines in ink
- you may wish to shade in the 'bars' to make them clearer
- give the graph a title.

1G DRAWING A ROSE DIAGRAM

A rose diagram compares the amount of something in different compass directions. You can draw a rose diagram in the following way:
- draw a small circle in the centre of the page
- from the edge of the circle, draw bars outwards in the direction of the eight compass points, in pencil (see Figure 1.5)
- use a protractor to ensure that the lines are drawn at the correct angle
- each bar shows the amount of something that occurs in that direction, for example in Figure 1.5 the bars show the **number of days** with winds from one direction
- find the greatest amount in any direction and work out a suitable scale (see Figure 1.5)
- using the scale, work out the length of each bar and shade them in, starting from the edge of the circle
- give the diagram a title and write a scale beside it.

Ⓕ Questions

Look at 1B.
Ⓕ1 Which technique would you use to find out the weather forecast for your local area?

Look at 1D and Figure 1.6.
Ⓕ2 (a) Copy the line graph in Figure 1.6.
(b) Complete the graph using the information in Figure 1.7.

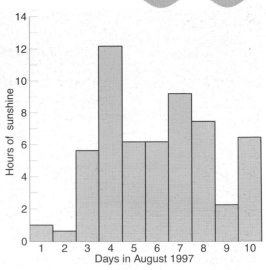

Figure 1.4 Sunshine in Glasgow, 1–10 August 1997

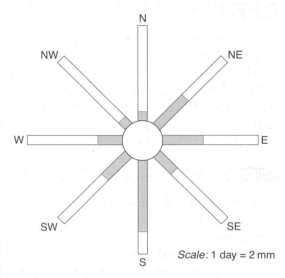

Scale: 1 day = 2 mm

Figure 1.5 Wind directions in Glasgow, July 1997

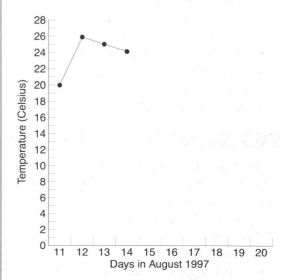

Figure 1.6 Maximum temperatures in Glasgow, 11–20 August 1997

Figure 1.7

Day in August 1997	Maximum temperature in Glasgow (°C)
11	20
12	26
13	25
14	24
15	23
16	25
17	22
18	23
19	23
20	28

Look at 1F and Figure 1.8.

F3 (a) Copy the bar graph in Figure 1.8.

(b) Complete the bar graph using the information in Figure 1.9.

Figure 1.9

Day in August 1997	Sunshine in Glasgow (hours)
11	2
12	3
13	6
14	5
15	3
16	7
17	4
18	8
19	1
20	7

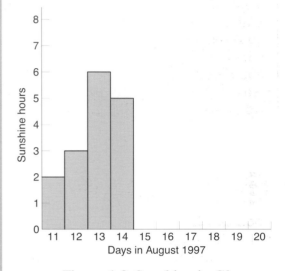

Figure 1.8 Sunshine in Glasgow, 11–20 August 1997

Look at Figures 1.10 and 1.11.

F4 Which table of information, Figure 1.10 or 1.11, would be better shown with (a) a line graph and (b) a bar graph?

Figure 1.10

Day in August 1997	Air pressure in Glasgow (mb)
1	1006
2	1020
3	1020
4	1025
5	1025
6	1022
7	1022
8	1017

Figure 1.11

Type of weather	Number of days
Fog	19
Thunder	9
Snow	11
Frost	23

Figure 1.12

Wind directions in Edinburgh	Number of days
North	1
North-east	5
East	5
South-east	3
South	9
South-west	4
West	3
North-west	1

G Questions

Look at 1B.

G1 Which technique would you use to find out the effects of a flood? Give a reason for your answer.

Look at 1D.

G2 Draw a line graph to show the information given in Figure 1.13.

Figure 1.13

Day in August 1997	Mean temperature in Glasgow (°C)
21	20
22	17
23	14
24	13
25	16
26	15
27	16
28	14
29	13
30	13
31	14

Look at 1F.

G3 Draw a bar graph to show the information given in Figure 1.14.

Figure 1.14

Day in August 1997	Rainfall in Glasgow (mm)
21	4
22	0
23	1
24	4
25	0
26	0
27	2
28	3
29	6
30	0
31	0

Look at Figures 1.10 and 1.11.

C4 Which table of information, Figure 1.10 or 1.11, would be better shown with a line graph? (See **F** Questions.) Give a reason for your answer.

Figure 1.15

Day in August 1997	Maximum temperature in Glasgow (°C)	Minimum temperature in Glasgow (°C)
21	22	18
22	21	13
23	19	9
24	17	9
25	21	12
26	21	9
27	19	14
28	19	10
29	18	9
30	19	7
31	19	9

Figure 1.16

Wind directions in Glasgow	Number of days
North	0
North-east	1
East	0
South-east	12
South	4
South-west	11
West	2
North-west	1

C Questions

Look at 1B.

C1 Which techniques would you use to find out the causes and effects of a severe gale? Give reasons for your choices.

C2 Draw a multiple line graph to show the information in Figure 1.15 opposite. Use the advice in 1E to help you.

C3 Draw a rose diagram to show the information in Figure 1.16, the table of wind directions opposite. Use the advice in 1G to help you.

Look at Figures 1.10, 1.11 and 1.12.

C4 Which table of information, Figure 1.10, 1.11 or 1.12, would be best shown by (a) a line graph, (b) a bar graph and (c) a rose diagram? (See **F** Questions.) Give a reason for your answer.

Measuring and Recording the Weather (1)

Core Text

2A THE ELEMENTS OF THE WEATHER

When people describe the weather they may be talking about any of the eight things listed in Figure 2.1 below. These are the main **elements** of the weather.

Figure 2.1

Weather element	Examples
Temperature	Hot, freezing
Rainfall/snowfall	Rain, dry
Wind speed	Windy, calm
Wind direction	Northerly
Cloud amount	Cloudy, overcast
Visibility	Clear, foggy
Air pressure	High pressure
Sunshine amount	Sunny

To describe the weather fully, the different elements have to be **measured** or **observed**.

2B MEASURING TEMPERATURE

Element:	temperature
Instrument:	maximum and minimum thermometer
Units:	degrees Celsius (or Centigrade) (°C)
Location:	in the shade

Temperature is measured by using a thermometer. Figure 2.2 shows a maximum and minimum thermometer. This instrument shows the highest and lowest temperatures since it was last read. The bottom of the metal pin or **index** on the right-hand side shows the maximum temperature. The bottom of the index on the left-hand side shows the minimum temperature. The mercury level shows the actual temperature at the time of reading.

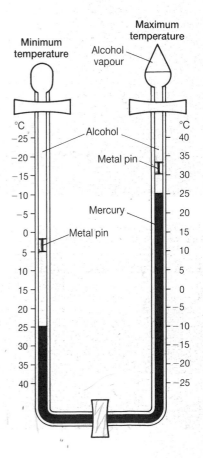

Figure 2.2 Maximum and minimum thermometer

Figure 2.3 describes how hot or cold different temperature readings are.

2C A STEVENSON SCREEN

Figure 2.4 shows a Stevenson Screen. This is a wooden box in which thermometers are placed. It allows the air temperature to be measured accurately. The box stands on legs 1 m long and is sited away from buildings so that it is not affected by the temperature of the ground or buildings.

2D MEASURING RAINFALL AND SNOWFALL

Element: rainfall, snowfall (precipitation)
Instrument: rain gauge
Units: millimetres (mm)
Location: away from buildings and walls that shelter it; on a non-splash surface

Rainfall and snowfall are measured with a **rain gauge** shown in Figure 2.5. This is a copper cylinder, sunk into the ground, with a funnel on top.

Figure 2.6 on page 15 is a guide to the conditions that produce different rainfall totals.

Core Questions

Look at 2A.

1 Name seven elements of the weather.
2 Copy and complete the table below by writing the correct weather element next to each word.

Description	Weather element
Hot	Temperature
Cloudy	
Foggy	
Rainy	
Calm	
South-westerly	
Sunny	
Low pressure	
Misty	
Breezy	
Hail	

Look at 2B and 2D.

3 Which instrument is used to measure (a) temperature and (b) rainfall?
4 What type of graph is used to show (a) temperature and (b) rainfall?

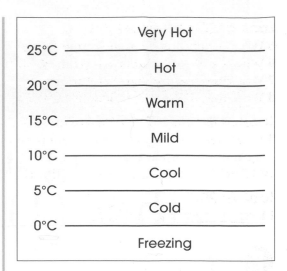

	Very Hot
25°C	
	Hot
20°C	
	Warm
15°C	
	Mild
10°C	
	Cool
5°C	
	Cold
0°C	
	Freezing

Figure 2.3 Temperature descriptions

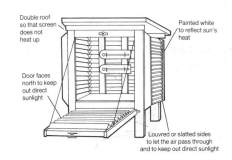

Double roof so that screen does not heat up

Painted white to reflect sun's heat

Door faces north to keep out direct sunlight

Louvred or slatted sides to let the air pass through and to keep out direct sunlight

Figure 2.4 A Stevenson Screen

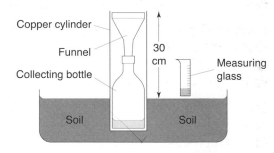

Copper cylinder

Funnel

Collecting bottle

30 cm

Measuring glass

Soil   Soil

Figure 2.5 A rain gauge

Look at 2C and Figure 2.4.

5 What is kept inside a Stevenson Screen?
6 Why is a Stevenson Screen painted white?
7 Why does a Stevenson Screen have slatted sides?
8 Why does a Stevenson Screen have legs 1 m long?

Look at the thermometer in Figure 2.2.

9 What has been (a) the maximum temperature and (b) the minimum temperature?
10 Which two liquids are used in this thermometer?

Look at 2D.

11 Where should a rain gauge be located?

F Questions

CASE STUDY OF STIRLING UNIVERSITY WEATHER STATION

Look at Figures 2.8 and 2.9, which show the weather station at Stirling University.

F1 Do you think this is a suitable location for a Stevenson Screen? Give reasons for your answer.

F2 Do you think this is a suitable location for a rain gauge? Give reasons for your answer.

Look at Figure 2.10. It shows the weather recorded at Stirling University in May 1995.

F3 Were the temperatures higher or lower than the average?

F4 Was the rainfall higher or lower than the average?

Look at Figure 2.15. It is a graph of temperatures during the first week in May 1995.

F5 Which was the warmest day?

F6 On which day was the lowest temperature recorded?

Look at Figure 2.16. It shows rainfall during the first week in May 1995.

F7 Which was the wettest day?

F8 How many dry days were there?

Look at Figure 2.12. It gives a weather forecast for May 2, 1995.

F9 Do you think this was an accurate forecast? Give reasons for your answer.

Rainfall on one day (mm)	Description
	Heavy rain for much of the day
12	
	Long periods of rain
6	
	Occasional showers
1	
	A little drizzle
Dry	

Figure 2.6 Descriptions of rainfall totals

G Questions

CASE STUDY OF STIRLING UNIVERSITY WEATHER STATION

Look at Figures 2.8 and 2.9, which show Stirling University Weather Station.

G1 What are the advantages and disadvantages of this location for (a) a Stevenson Screen and (b) a rain gauge?

Look at Figure 2.11. It shows the weather recorded at Stirling University in May 1995.

G2 Compare the weather in May 1995 with the average for that time of year.

Look at Figure 2.15. It shows the temperatures during the first week in May 1995.

G3 Describe the changes in the maximum temperature.

G4 Describe the changes in the minimum temperature.

Look at Figures 2.12 and 2.13. They show weather forecasts for May 3rd and 4th, 1995.

G5 On which day was the weather forecast better, the 3rd or the 4th? Give reasons for your answer.

CASE STUDY OF STIRLING UNIVERSITY WEATHER STATION

Figure 2.7

Stirling University Weather Station was set up in 1971 to provide information for the Biology Department. In 1994 it was moved a short distance to its present location, shown in Figure 2.9. The weather station has a Stevenson Screen, which contains a maximum thermometer, minimum thermometer, a dry-bulb thermometer and a wet-bulb thermometer. Near the Stevenson Screen is a rain gauge and a soil thermometer. Readings are taken every day at 9.00 a.m. and these are sent to the Meteorological Office monthly.

Figure 2.8 Stirling University weather station

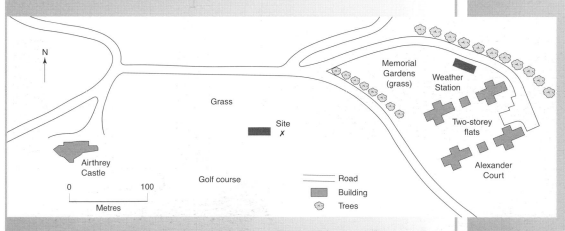

Figure 2.9 Location of Stirling University weather station

RESOURCES

Figure 2.10

	May 1–7 1995	Average for one week in May
Temperature	13°C	11°C
Rainfall	6.0 mm	11.1 mm

Figure 2.11

	May 1–7 1995	Average for one week in May
Minimum temperature	19.0°C	16.5°C
Maximum temperature	7.5°C	5.5°C
Rainfall	6.0 mm	11.1 mm

Figure 2.12

Weather forecast for 2nd May

Today will be mainly dry, although there will be a little rain in the afternoon and temperatures will only reach 15°C. It will stay cloudy during the evening and will remain quite warm with temperatures no lower than 11°C.

Figure 2.13

Weather forecast for 3rd May

It will be cloudy with sunny intervals and temperatures should reach 21°C during the afternoon. The night will be cold, temperatures falling to 6°C. It will remain dry all day.

Figure 2.14

Weather forecast for 4th May

It will be dry and sunny all day, with temperatures rising to 22°C. It will quickly cool down at night and temperatures will drop to only 3°C.

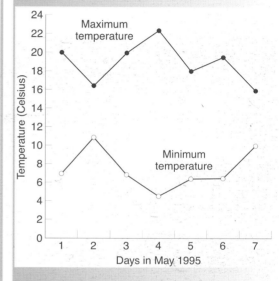

Figure 2.15 Maximum and minimum temperatures in Glasgow, May 1995

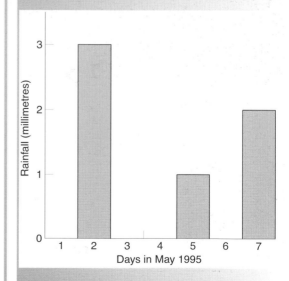

Figure 2.16 Rainfall in Stirling, May 1995

Extension Text

2E THE WEATHER ELEMENTS

Temperature and **precipitation** (rain, snow, hail, sleet) are the main elements of the weather, but there are at least ten elements altogether (Figure 2.17).

Figure 2.17

Weather element

Temperature
Precipitation
Humidity
Wind speed
Wind direction
Cloud amount
Cloud type
Visibility
Atmospheric pressure
Thunder and lightning

2F MEASURING HUMIDITY

Figure 2.18

Element:	humidity
Instrument:	hygrometer (or wet and dry bulb thermometer)
Units:	percentage (%)
Location:	in a Stevenson Screen

Words such as 'humid', 'muggy' and 'clammy' describe the humidity, that is the amount of water vapour in the air.

The air can only hold a limited amount of water vapour, but warm air can hold more than cold air. When the air is holding all the water it can, it is said to be **saturated**. A slight fall in temperature will result in condensation and water droplets will form, making cloud or fog. The temperature at which this happens is called the **dew point**.

Precipitation only takes place in saturated air so it is useful to know the amount of water in the air relative to the amount in saturated air. This is called the **relative humidity** and is given as a percentage. A relative humidity of 100 per cent means saturated air. The nearer to 100 per cent, the nearer the air is to saturation point.

To work out the relatively humidity a **hygrometer** is used, as shown in Figure 2.19. The wet bulb temperature is taken and subtracted from the dry bulb temperature (called the 'depression' of the wet bulb). Figure 2.20 is then used to calculate the relative humidity.

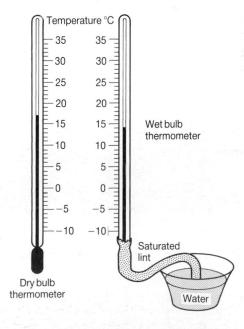

Figure 2.19 A hygrometer

Figure 2.20 Table for calculating relative humidity

Dry bulb temperature	Depression or declination of the wet bulb							
°C	0.5	1.0	1.5	2.0	2.5	3.0	3.5	4.0
0	91	82	73	65	56	48	39	31
1	91	83	75	66	58	50	42	34
2	92	84	76	68	60	52	45	37
3	92	84	77	69	62	54	47	40
4	92	85	78	70	63	56	49	42
5	93	86	79	72	65	58	51	45
6	93	86	79	73	66	60	53	47
7	93	87	80	74	67	61	55	49
8	94	89	81	75	69	63	57	51
9	94	88	82	76	70	64	58	53
10	94	88	82	76	71	65	60	54
11	94	88	83	77	72	66	61	56
12	94	89	83	78	73	68	62	57
13	95	89	84	79	74	69	64	59
14	95	90	84	79	74	70	65	60
15	95	90	85	80	75	71	66	61
16	95	90	85	81	76	71	67	63
17	95	90	86	81	77	72	68	64
18	95	91	86	82	77	73	69	65
19	95	91	86	82	78	74	70	65
20	96	91	87	83	78	74	70	66
21	96	91	87	83	79	75	71	67
22	96	92	88	83	80	76	72	68

E Questions

Read the Extension Text.

E1 What is meant by the term 'humidity'?

E2 With which instrument is humidity measured?

E3 What is meant by the term 'saturated air'?

E4 Which can hold more water vapour: cold or warm air?

E5 Copy the information below and use Figure 2.20 to complete it.

Dry bulb temperature (°C)	Wet bulb temperature (°C)	Relative humidity
12	11	
20	16	

E6 To which elements of the weather does the forecast below refer?

Today will start misty, but the wind will increase and it will become warm, humid and overcast, with a possibility of rain later.

C Questions

CASE STUDY OF STIRLING UNIVERSITY WEATHER STATION

Look at Figure 2.9. It shows the location of Stirling University Weather Station and an alternative location, site X.

C1 Describe the different points of view people would have towards moving the weather station to site X.

Look at Figure 2.15. It shows the temperature at Stirling University in the first week of May 1995.

C2 Describe the relationship between the maximum and minimum temperatures.

Look at Figures 2.15 and 2.16.

C3 Compare the maximum and minimum temperatures on the dry days with those on the wet days.

Look at Figures 2.12, 2.13 and 2.14. They show weather forecasts for May 2, 3 and 4, 1995.

C4 Which was the most accurate forecast? Give reasons for your answer.

Measuring and Recording the Weather (2)

Core Text

3A MEASURING WIND DIRECTION

Element:	wind direction
Instrument:	wind vane (or weather vane)
Units:	points of the compass
Location:	in the open, away from shelter

A wind vane, shown in Figure 3.1, measures wind direction. The arrow points to the direction the wind is coming from.

3B MEASURING WIND SPEED

Element:	wind speed
Instrument:	anemometer
Units:	kilometres per hour (km/h)
Location:	10 metres above the ground, away from buildings

Wind speed can be measured with an **anemometer**, shown in Figure 3.2. This has three hollow metal cups that catch the wind and spin around. The faster the wind blows, the faster the cups spin. A reading is given on the speedometer underneath.

3C MEASURING AIR PRESSURE

Elements:	atmospheric or air pressure
Instrument:	barometer or barograph
Units:	millibars (mb)
Location:	indoors

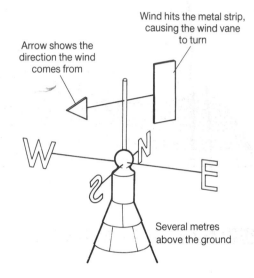

Figure 3.1 A wind vane

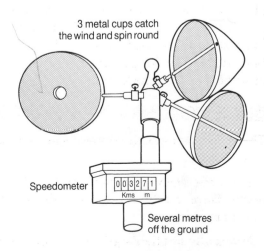

Figure 3.2 An anemometer

Air pressure is the pressure that air makes because of its weight. Sensitive instruments called **barometers** measure slight changes in air pressure. The pressure is shown by an arrow on the face of the barometer. A metal indicator shows the air pressure at the last time the barometer was reset.

A **barograph**, shown in Figure 3.3, records the air pressure all the time. A pen on an arm traces a line on paper attached to a drum, which makes one rotation a week.

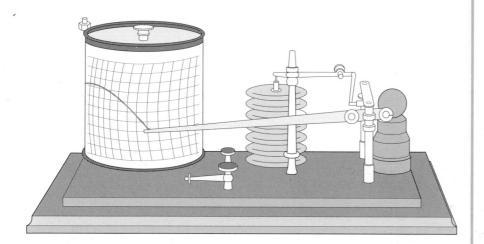

Figure 3.3 A barograph

3D MEASURING SUNSHINE

Element:	sunshine
Instrument:	sunshine recorder
Units:	hours (h)
Location:	in the open, away from shade

A **sunshine recorder**, shown in Figure 3.4, is a glass ball, mounted on a frame, with a strip of card behind it. When the sun shines, the glass concentrates the rays onto the card, which burns. Because the sun appears to move during the day, different parts of the card are burned, as shown in Figure 3.5. If there is no sunshine, there is no burn mark. The longer the burn mark on the card, the more hours of sunshine there have been.

3E RECORDING THE WEATHER

The different weather elements are measured and recorded in various ways.

There are **weather stations** all over Britain and throughout the world. Here, all the elements of the weather are recorded at set times each day.

Automatic weather stations are used in areas where few people live, for example deserts. They record the air pressure, temperature, wind and humidity.

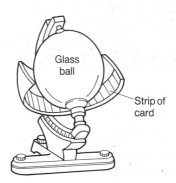

Figure 3.4 A sunshine recorder

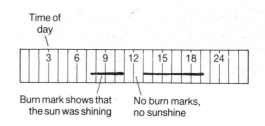

Figure 3.5 Sunshine recording card

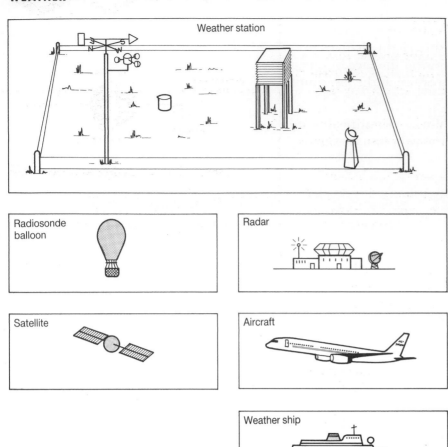

Figure 3.6 Methods of recording weather information

Radiosonde balloons are sent into the upper air, carrying weather instruments. They send back information on temperature, air pressure and humidity by radio.

Satellites orbit the earth and take photographs of the clouds and pressure systems.

Radar is used to find out where rain, snow or hail is falling and the direction in which it is moving.

Aircraft carry instruments that record the wind and the temperature.

Weather ships record information on all the weather elements in the seas and oceans.

3F WEATHER FORECASTING

Details of the weather from all over Britain and the world are sent to the Meteorological Office in Bracknell, near London. Here millions of items of weather information are fed into computers, which quickly print out weather maps. The weather maps are then studied by weather forecasters, who predict what the weather will be. Their forecasts are sent to TV and radio stations, newspapers and British Telecom so that everyone can know the forecasts as soon as possible.

3G THE ACCURACY OF FORECASTS

Weather forecasts are becoming more accurate for several reasons:

1 there are more weather satellites in space, which allow forecasters to detect high and low pressure areas and track which way they are moving,

2 there is now a network of weather radars that show how heavy the rain is all over the country and which way and how fast the bands of rain are moving, and

3 more advanced computers make calculations very quickly and have speeded up forecasts. They are also programmed to use all the information they have on past weather to make forecasts.

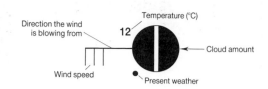

Figure 3.7 A weather station circle

3H WEATHER STATION CIRCLES

Figure 3.7 shows a weather station circle. It is used to display the weather at any one place. A weather station circle uses different symbols to show temperature, cloud, wind and rainfall. The meaning of these symbols is given in Figure 3.8.

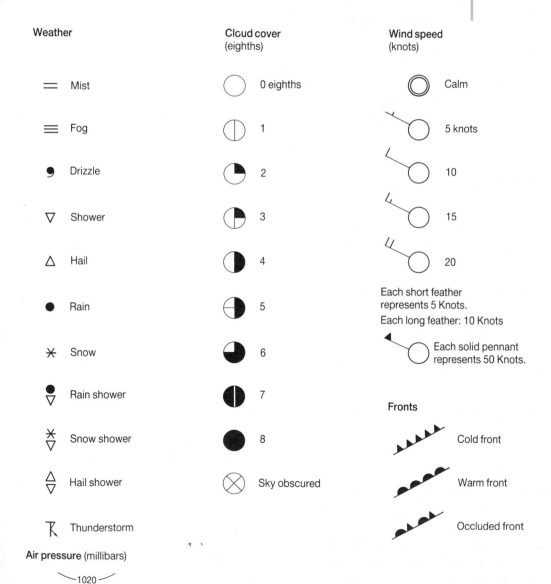

Figure 3.8 The symbols used in weather station circles

Core Questions

Look at 3A, 3B, 3C and 3D.

1 Match the weather elements below to the instruments used to measure them.

Element	Instrument
Air pressure	Wind vane
Wind speed	Barometer
Wind direction	Sunshine recorder
Sunshine	Anemometer

Look at 3A.

2 Why should wind direction not be measured near a building?

3 Does a westerly wind blow from the west or to the west?

Look at 3B.

4 Where should wind speed be measured?

Look at 3C.

5 In which units is air pressure measured?

6 Which instrument, a barometer or a barograph, records air pressure all the time?

Look at 3D.

7 Describe how a sunshine recorder works.

Look at 3E.

8 Apart from weather stations, name three other ways of finding out weather information.

Look at 3G.

9 Why are weather forecasts becoming more accurate?

Look at Figures 3.7 and 3.8.

10 According to the weather station circle, what is (a) the temperature, (b) the cloud amount, (c) the wind speed, (d) the wind direction and (e) the present weather?

Ⓕ Questions

CASE STUDY OF PRESTWICK WEATHER STATION

Look at Figure 3.10. It shows the weather station at Prestwick.

Ⓕ1 Why is this a good location for the sunshine recorder?

Look at Figure 3.11. It shows the wind vane and anemometer on a high mast.

Ⓕ2 Do you think this is a suitable location for the wind vane? Give reasons for your answer.

Look at Figure 3.13.

F3 On which date was (a) the highest air pressure and, (b) the lowest air pressure?

F4 In what way did air pressure change on 12th November?

Look at Figure 3.18. It shows the weather in Prestwick for one week in November 1996.

F5 Which was the best day to go walking? Give a reason for your answer.

Look at Figure 3.20. It shows wind directions during the second week in November 1996.

F6 (a) From which direction did most winds blow?
(b) From which directions did no winds blow?

Look at Figures 3.8 and 3.19.

F7 Draw a weather station circle to show the weather in Prestwick at 12.00 hours on (a) November 3 and (b) November 4, 1996.

G Questions

CASE STUDY OF PRESTWICK WEATHER STATION

Look at Figure 3.10 which shows Prestwick Weather Station.

G1 Do you think the sunshine recorder is in a suitable location? Give reasons for your answer.

Look at Figure 3.11 which shows the anemometer and wind vane on a high mast.

G2 Do you think the anemometer is in a suitable location? Give reasons for your answer.

Look at Figure 3.13.

G3 Describe the changes in air pressure at Prestwick during the second week in November 1996.

Look at Figure 3.21.

G4 Describe the changes in wind force during the same week.

Look at Figures 3.15 and 3.20.

G5 Compare the wind directions during the first and second weeks in November 1996.

Look at Figures 3.16 and 3.18.

G6 Was the weather forecast for November 3 accurate? Give reasons for your answer.

Look at Figures 3.8 and 3.19.

G7 Draw a weather station circle to show the weather in Prestwick at 12.00 hours on (a) November 8 and (b) November 9, 1996.

CASE STUDY OF PRESTWICK AIRPORT

Figure 3.9

Introduction

Prestwick Weather Station is located at Prestwick Airport, 5 kilometres north of Ayr on the Firth of Clyde. It is run by the Royal Navy Air Service, who need the weather information to brief their air crews before they fly. The weather station was set up in 1971.

Some weather elements, such as temperature, wind speed and cloud amount, are recorded continuously. Others are observed every hour, day and night. All the information is sent immediately to the Meteorological Office in Bracknell.

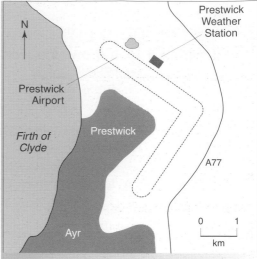

Figure 3.12 Location of Prestwick weather station

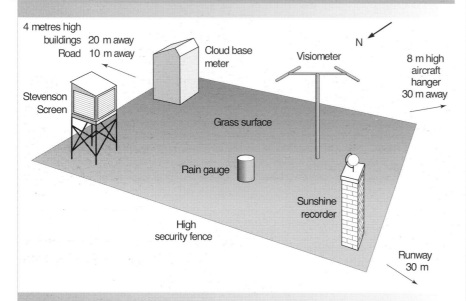

Figure 3.10 Prestwick weather station

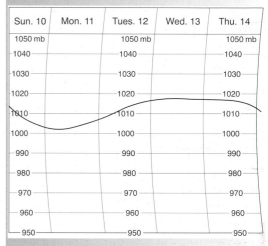

Figure 3.13 Barograph recording sheet for November 10–14, 1996

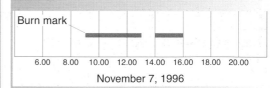

November 7, 1996

Figure 3.14 Sunshine recording strip

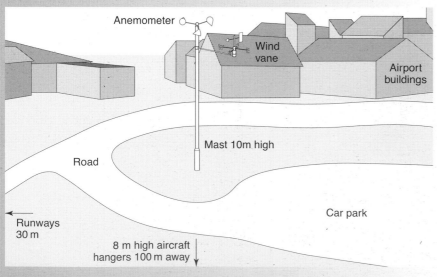

Figure 3.11 Prestwick's anemometer and wind vane

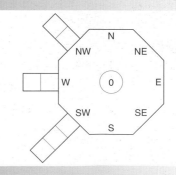

Figure 3.15 Wind rose for November 3–9, 1996

★ RESOURCES ★

Figure 3.16

Weather forecast for 3rd November

The winds today will reach 20 knots from the south-west. It will remain cloudy all day.

Figure 3.17

Weather forecast for 4th November

The strong westerly winds will reach gale force by the middle of the day. The morning will be cloudy but the afternoon should be sunny.

Figure 3.18

Date	Hours of sunshine	Average air pressure (mb)	Wind direction at 12.00 hours	Wind force at 12.00 hours
3 November	0.1	998	SW	5
4 November	2.3	983	SW	8
5 November	3.5	1001	NW	6
6 November	1.4	983	W	4
7 November	5.9	1005	W	6
8 November	7.0	1012	SW	7
9 November	5.4	1019	NW	6

Figure 3.19

The weather at Prestwick at 12.00 hours 3–9 November 1996

	3rd	4th	5th	6th	7th	8th	9th
Temperature (°C)	13	10	8	9	7	8	8
Wind speed (knots)	20	40	25	15	25	30	25
Wind direction	SW	SW	NW	W	W	SW	NW
Cloud cover	8	4	3	Sky obscured	7	3	4
Present weather	Rain	Showers	Dry	Mist	Showers	Dry	Showers

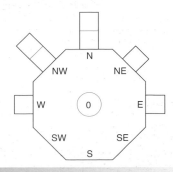

Figure 3.20 Wind rose for November 10–16, 1996

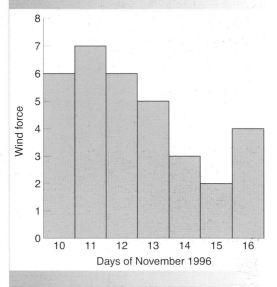

Figure 3.21 Wind force at Prestwick, November 10–16, 1996

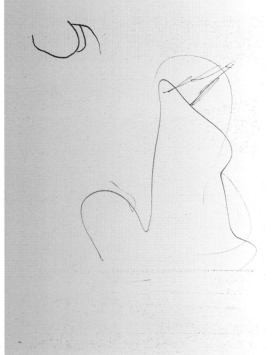

27

Extension Text

3E OBSERVING WIND SPEED

Figure 3.22

The Beaufort Scale

Force	Observation	Description	Wind speed (km/h)
0	Calm	Calm, smoke rises vertically	0
1	Light air	Direction of wind shown by smoke, but not by wind vanes	3
2	Light breeze	Wind felt on face, leaves rustle	8
3	Gentle breeze	Leaves and small twigs in constant motion, wind extends light flag	16
4	Moderate breeze	Raises dust and loose paper; small branches are moved	24
5	Fresh breeze	Small trees in leaf begin to sway	34
6	Strong breeze	Large branches in motion; whistling heard in telegraph wires; umbrellas used with difficulty	45
7	Near gale	Whole trees in motion; inconvenience felt when walking against wind	56
8	Gale	Breaks twigs off trees; generally impedes progress	67
9	Strong gale	Slight structural damage occurs (chimney pots and slates removed)	80
10	Storm	Seldom experienced inland; trees uprooted; considerable structural damage occurs	94
11	Violent storm	Very rarely experienced; accompanied by widespread damage	109
12	Hurricane	—	117+

The **Beaufort Scale**, shown in Figure 3.22, is used to estimate the speed or force of the wind. The effects of the wind on common objects, such as smoke and trees, are used to estimate the wind force. The maximum wind force on the Beaufort Scale is 12.

3F OBSERVING CLOUD AMOUNT

Element:	cloud amount
Units:	eighths of the sky (or **oktas**)
Location:	where the whole sky can be seen

The cloud amount is worked out by estimating how many eighths (or **oktas**) of the sky are covered in cloud. No oktas indicates a cloudless sky whereas eight oktas describes a sky completely covered in cloud.

3G OBSERVING VISIBILITY

Element:	visibility
Units:	metres or kilometres
Location:	where it is possible to see a long way

The visibility is the furthest distance that can be seen. To work out this distance you need to know how far away the different features in your view are.

E Questions

Read the Extension Text.

E1 What is the highest number on the Beaufort Scale?

E2 Explain how the Beaufort Scale can be used to estimate wind speed.

E3 Describe how cloud cover is observed.

E4 Describe how visibility is observed.

C Questions

CASE STUDY OF PRESTWICK WEATHER STATION

Look at Figures 3.10 and 3.11. They show the location of the weather instruments at Prestwick Weather Station.

C1 Suggest why the anemometer and wind vane have not been relocated next to the other instruments.

C2 Suggest why the sunshine recorder is not located next to the mast holding the anemometer and wind vane.

Look at Figure 3.18.

C3 Describe the relationship between the air pressure and the amount of sunshine during the first week in November 1996.

C4 Describe the relationship between the wind speed and wind force during the first week in November 1996.

Look at Figures 3.16, 3.17 and 3.18.

C5 Which was the more accurate forecast – the forecast for the 3rd or 4th November? Give reasons for your answer.

Look at Figure 3.19.

C6 Draw a weather station circle to show the weather in Prestwick at 12.00 hours on (a) 6 November and (b) 7 November 1996.

UNIT ④

Weather Systems

Core Text

4A AIR STREAMS

The weather in Britain and the rest of Europe depends on the winds that blow over us. These winds come from many different areas. Winds that come from a particular area are called **air streams**. Five main air streams affect us and they bring different types of weather, as shown in Figure 4.1.

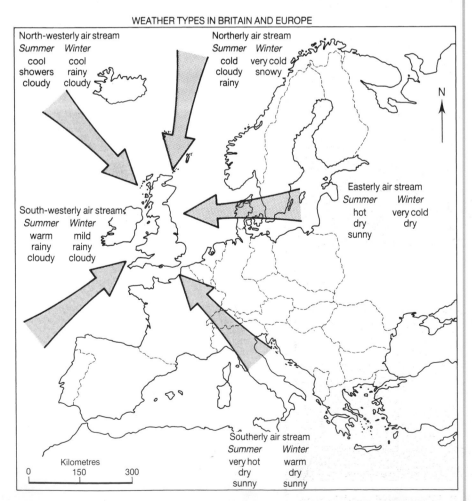

WEATHER TYPES IN BRITAIN AND EUROPE

North-westerly air stream
Summer	*Winter*
cool	cool
showers	rainy
cloudy	cloudy

Northerly air stream
Summer	*Winter*
cold	very cold
cloudy	snowy
rainy	

Easterly air stream
Summer	*Winter*
hot	very cold
dry	dry
sunny	

South-westerly air streams
Summer	*Winter*
warm	mild
rainy	rainy
cloudy	cloudy

Southerly air stream
Summer	*Winter*
very hot	warm
dry	dry
sunny	sunny

N

Kilometres
0   150   300

Figure 4.1a Air streams affecting Britain

Air stream	Type of weather
From the ocean	Rainy, cloudy
From the land	Dry, clear
From the south	Warm
From the north	Cold

4B WARM AND COLD FRONTS

The line along which one air stream meets another is called a **front**. The two air streams do not mix. The warmer lighter air stream always rises over the colder, denser air stream.

When the warmer air rises, it cools down. The water in the air turns to water droplets. Millions of water droplets in the air are called **clouds**. These droplets become bigger and bigger until they are heavy enough to fall as rain.

Fronts do not usually stay still. They can move at over 50 km/h and, as they pass over us, they bring cloud and usually rain.

Warm fronts bring steady rain
Cold fronts bring heavy rain

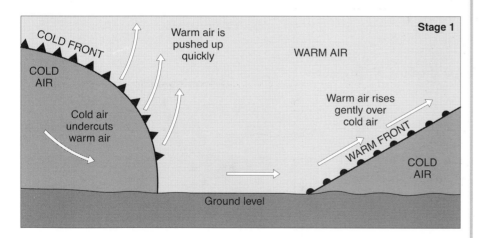

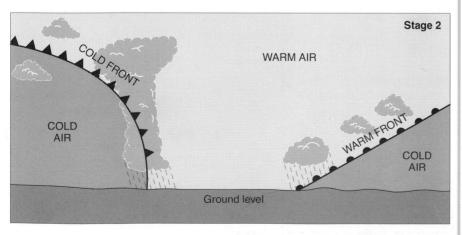

Figure 4.2 Warm and cold fronts

4C AIR PRESSURE AND WINDS

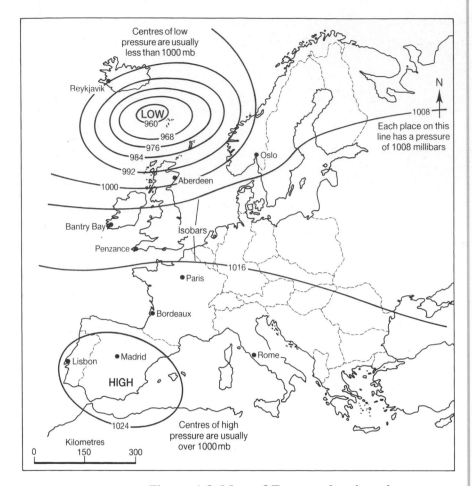

Figure 4.3 **Map of Europe showing air pressure**

Labels in figure: Centres of low pressure are usually less than 1000 mb; Reykjavik; LOW 960; 968; 976; 984; 992; 1000; Oslo; Aberdeen; Bantry Bay; Isobars; Penzance; 1008; Each place on this line has a pressure of 1008 millibars; N; 1016; Paris; Bordeaux; Rome; Lisbon; Madrid; HIGH; 1024; Centres of high pressure are usually over 1000 mb; Kilometres 0 150 300

The winds and air streams that affect us depend on air pressure. Air pressure is shown on maps by **isobars**. These are lines joining places that have the same air pressure. Once isobars have been drawn, as in Figure 4.3, it is easy to see where the areas of high pressure and low pressure are.

Winds blow from high pressure areas to low pressure areas. However, they do not blow straight from high to low pressure but at an angle, because of the west–east rotation of the earth.

4D DEPRESSIONS OR LOW PRESSURE SYSTEMS

Depressions are low pressure systems. They usually move from west to east across Europe. Normally, they have warm and cold fronts in them, so they bring cloud and rain. Between the fronts is a **warm sector**, where the air is not rising. Here the weather is warmer and drier.

4E ANTICYCLONES OR HIGH PRESSURE SYSTEMS

Anticyclones are high pressure systems. In an anticyclone the air is falling, so the weather is dry and sunny and quite calm. In winter, high pressures bring very cold weather to Britain. In summer they bring very hot weather.

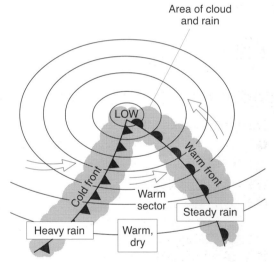

Figure 4.4 **A low pressure system**

Labels in figure: Area of cloud and rain; LOW; Cold front; Warm front; Warm sector; Steady rain; Heavy rain; Warm, dry

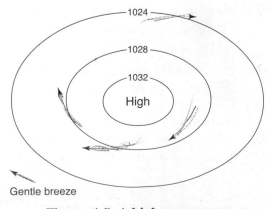

Figure 4.5 **A high pressure system**

Labels in figure: 1024; 1028; 1032; High; Gentle breeze

Core Questions

Look at Figure 4.1.

1 What types of weather do these air streams bring in summer:
   (a) southerly
   (b) easterly
   (c) north westerly
   (d) south westerly?

Look at 4B.

2 What is a front?
3 What type of weather is brought by a warm front?
4 What are clouds made of?

Look at 4C and Figure 4.6.

5 Which is a low pressure area in Figure 4.6, A or B?
6 The lines in the diagram join places that have the same pressure. What are these lines called?

Look at 4D.

7 What is a low pressure system called?
8 Describe the types of weather brought by a depression.

Look at 4E.

9 What is a high pressure system called?
10 What types of weather do high pressures bring in (a) winter and (b) summer?

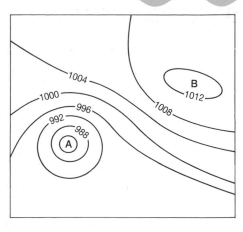

Figure 4.6 A map showing air pressure

F Questions

CASE STUDY OF EUROPE, FEBRUARY 1990

Look at Figure 4.10.

F1 Which do you think was colder: the first or second week in February? Give a reason for your answer.

Look at Figure 4.11.

F2 Which place has the higher pressure:
   (a) Liverpool or London?
   (b) Glasgow or Amsterdam?

F3 In which place is it more likely to be raining: Liverpool or Oslo? Give a reason for your answer.

Look at 4D and Figure 4.7.

F4 Do you agree with what the man is saying in Figure 4.7? Give a reason for your answer.

Look at Figure 4.11.

F5 Do you think the weather in Vienna is good for sightseeing? Give a reason for your answer.

F6 Do you think Oslo will have rain in the next 24 hours? Give a reason for your answer.

F7 Which of the weather details below (A or B) describes Madrid's weather? Give a reason for your answer.

A: calm and 1/8th cloud
B: windy and 6/8ths cloud

Figure 4.7

⒢ Questions

■■ CASE STUDY OF EUROPE, FEBRUARY 1990

Look at Figure 4.11.

⒢1 Describe the air pressure over Europe on 17 February.

⒢2 Which place is likely to be having the heaviest rain: Liverpool, London or Amsterdam? Give reasons for your answer.

⒢3 Two people disagree as to whether Prague will get rain in the next 24 hours. Describe the arguments they would give.

Figure 4.8 Central London

⒢4 Figure 4.8 shows heavy rain falling in London on 17 February. Was the photograph taken in the morning, afternoon or evening? Give reasons for your answer.

⒢5 Which of the descriptions below (A or B) describes the weather in Glasgow on 17 February and which describes the weather in Prague? Give reasons for your answer.

	Cloud amount (eighths)	Wind speed (km/h)
A	3	5
B	7	25

Look at the box below.

⒢6 Do you think Vienna's weather is typical of an anticyclone? Give reasons for your answer.

Vienna's weather at 12.00, 17 February:
0°C; cloudy; windy; dry; 1025 mb

CASE STUDY OF EUROPE, 17 FEBRUARY 1990

Figure 4.9

Introduction

The weather in Europe is regularly affected by depressions, which come from the Atlantic Ocean and travel eastwards. On 17 February 1990 one of these depressions had reached Britain. Over the next 24 hours it moved away to the east, gradually filling in.

Figure 4.10

Weather Report for February 1990

For most of the first week there was a southerly air stream over parts of Britain. During the second week, there was a north-westerly air stream. The third week saw south-westerly winds ...

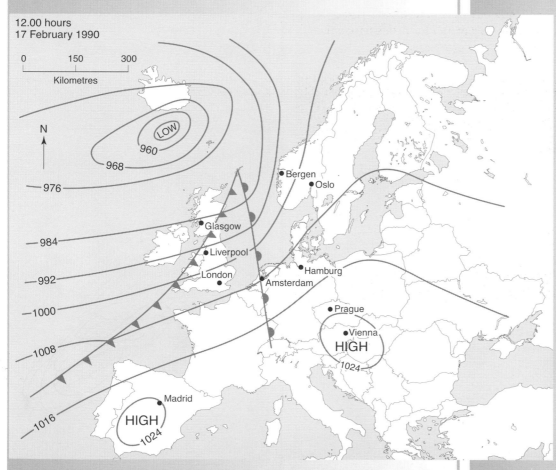

Figure 4.11 Weather chart for 12.00 hours, 17 February 1990

★ *RESOURCES* ★

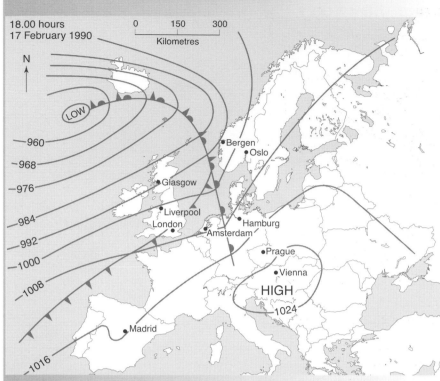

18.00 hours
17 February 1990

0   150   300
Kilometres

N

LOW

—960
—968
—976
—984
—992
—1000
—1008
—1016

Bergen
Oslo
Glasgow
Liverpool
London
Amsterdam
Hamburg
Prague
Vienna
HIGH
—1024
Madrid

Figure 4.12 Weather chart for 18.00 hours, 17 February 1990

Figure 4.13

Forecast A

Dry at 12.00, becoming cloudy with heavy rain, but soon clearing to give brighter, colder weather

Forecast B

Dry at 12.00, very heavy rain will soon follow; remaining cold all day

Forecast C

Dry at 12.00, becoming cloudy with steady rain before midnight

Figure 4.14

Weather in Vienna, 17 February

Air pressure	1025 mb
Wind speed	Force 4
Maximum temperature	5°C
Minimum temperature	−5°C
Cloud amount	7 oktas
Cloud type	Cumulus
Humidity	90%
Visibility	More than 30 km

Extension Text

4F AIR MASSES AND AIR STREAMS

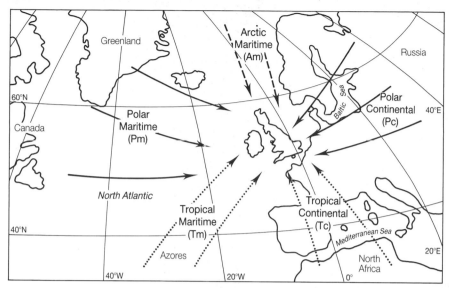

Figure 4.15 Air streams affecting the British Isles

An **air mass** is a large volume of air that has similar characteristics because it has remained in an area for a long time. When an air mass starts to move to another area, it is called an **air stream**. It will take with it all the characteristics it had. The main air streams affecting Britain are shown in Figure 4.15. They are given names according to where they begin as air masses in Figure 4.16.

Figure 4.16

Type of air stream	Location of air mass	Associated weather
Continental (c)	Over a land mass	Dry
Maritime (m)	Over an ocean	Rainy
Equatorial (E)	Near the Equator	Hot
Tropical (T)	Near the Tropics	Warm
Polar (P)	Near the Arctic Circle	Cold
Arctic (A)	Near the North Pole	Very cold

4G THE DEVELOPMENT OF A DEPRESSION

Between latitudes 40° and 45° many tropical air streams meet polar air streams. Where they meet is called the **polar front** (stage 1 in Figure 4.17). The line or zone where they meet is not straight but wavy so the warm air makes a wedge into the cold air (stage 2). At the top of the wedge or wave, a low pressure develops and winds start to blow around it in an anticlockwise direction (stage 3). At the warm front, the wedge of warm air in the warm sector rises over the cold air. At the cold front, the cold air pushes its way under the warm air. The cold front moves faster than the warm front. It eventually catches it and an **occluded front** forms (stage 4). At the occluded front, the cold air pushes all the warm air upwards rapidly. This causes short periods of torrential rain. When all the warm air has finally disappeared, the depression no longer exists.

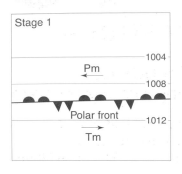

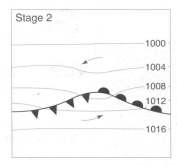

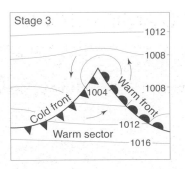

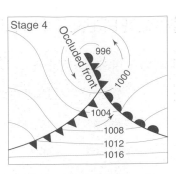

Figure 4.17 Stages in the formation of a depression

4H CROSS-SECTION THROUGH A DEPRESSION

Figure 4.19 shows a vertical section through a depression. Five stages are shown on the section. As a depression travels over an area, it brings the following sequence of weather:

Stage one   a few high clouds; dry; SE wind

Stage two   clouds are thicker and lower; air pressure falls; steady prolonged rain; warm front passes

Stage three   rain stops and the sky clears; wind veers from SE to SW; temperature rises; pressure stops falling

Stage four   clouds build up; heavy rain falls; cold front passes

Stage five   wind changes from SW to NW; heavy rain stops; air pressure rises; clouds are fewer

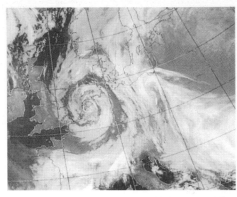

Figure 4.18 Satellite photo of a depression east of Britain

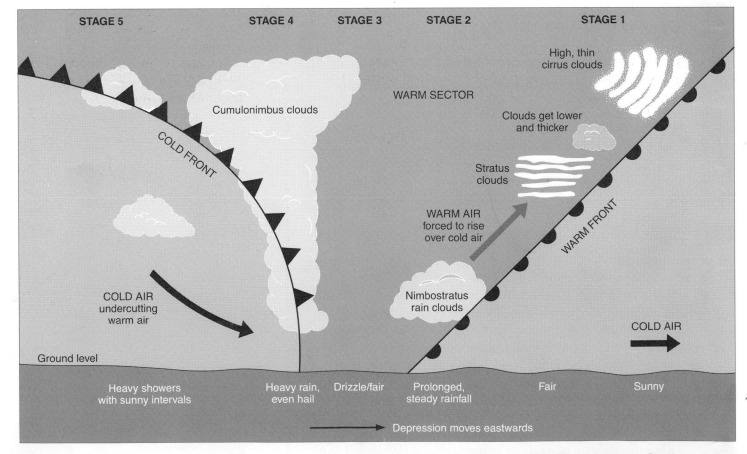

Figure 4.19 The passage of a depression

4I DEPRESSIONS AND ANTICYCLONES

Figure 4.20

	Depression	Anticyclone
Air movement	Upwards	Downwards
Air pressure	Low	High
Wind direction	Anticlockwise, towards centre of low pressure	Clockwise, away from centre of high pressure
Isobars	Close together	Far apart
Associated weather	Short sunny spells; longer periods of cloud, rain and wind	Dry; usually sunny; light winds; nights may be cold
Frequency	All year, but most in winter	Occasionally in summer and winter

E Questions

Read the Extension Text.

E1 Describe and explain the weather brought by (a) a tropical maritime air stream and (b) a polar continental air stream.

E2 Depressions form when which two air streams meet?

E3 Describe what happens to the air at (a) a warm front, (b) a cold front and (c) an occluded front.

E4 Describe how (a) wind direction, (b) cloud amount and (c) precipitation change as a depression passes over.

E5 Explain why there is little chance of rain at the centre of an anticyclone.

C Questions

CASE STUDY OF EUROPE, FEBRUARY 1990

Look at Figures 4.11 and 4.12.

C1 Compare the weather in Amsterdam at 12.00 and 18.00 on 17 February.

Look at Figure 4.12.

C2 Weather forecasts often give the possibility of rain as a percentage, for example 40% chance of rain today. What is the percentage chance of rain in Oslo before midnight on 17 February? Give reasons for your answer.

Look at Figure 4.13.

C3 Figure 4.13 shows the forecasts for Bergen, Hamburg and London for the 12 hours after 12.00 on 17 February. Match the forecasts (A, B and C) to the three places. Give reasons for your choices.

Look at Figure 4.14.

C4 Do you agree with the statement below? Give reasons for your answer.
'The weather in Vienna on 17 February was typical of winter anticyclonic conditions.'

UNIT ⑤

The Effects of the Weather

Core Text

5A THE EFFECTS OF THE WEATHER

The weather affects everyone, whether they are at home, at work or at play. Some weather conditions people enjoy; others bring problems. Some of these problems can be overcome.

5B HIGH PRESSURE CONDITIONS IN SUMMER

Weather: hot and sunny; long periods with little rain (called **droughts**)

Who likes: holidaymakers/sportspeople

Who dislikes	Reasons	Solutions
Farmers	Crops grow badly without rain	Put extra water on fields (**irrigation**)
Water authorities	Reservoirs are short of water	Restrict water, for example hosepipe ban
Foresters	Fires break out easily	Use fire towers
Office/factory workers	Too hot to work properly	Air conditioning

5C LOW PRESSURE CONDITIONS IN SUMMER

Weather: cool, cloudy, rainy, windy weather

Who likes: water authorities/fishermen

Who dislikes	Reasons	Solutions
Farmers	Wind flattens crops; crops do not ripen without sun	Shelter belts of trees Greenhouses
Holidaymakers	Sunbathing and sightseeing not possible	Indoor facilities
Outdoor sportspeople	Interrupts events, for example cricket, tennis matches	All weather courts and tracks

5D HIGH PRESSURE CONDITIONS IN WINTER

Weather: long periods of very cold weather; snow, ice and fog

Who likes: winter sportspeople, for example skiers

Who dislikes	Reasons	Solutions
Farmers	No grass for animals to eat; animals can be buried in snow	Give animals extra food; bring animals inside
Drivers/pilots	Ice and fog make driving and flying dangerous	Use snow ploughs, grit roads
People at home	High heating bills; pipes burst	Insulate houses; 'lag' pipes
Sportspeople	Difficult to play outdoors, for example football	Undersoil heating

5E LOW PRESSURE CONDITIONS IN WINTER

Weather: mild, cloudy, rainy, windy weather

Who likes: water authorities

Who dislikes	Reasons	Solutions
Outdoor workers	Difficult to work outdoors	Lay off workers
People at home	Damage to houses by gales, floods	Flood protection schemes
Lorry drivers	Difficult to drive high-sided lorries in gales	Warning signs on roads
Sportspeople	Waterlogged pitches	Drain the land

Core Questions

Look at 5B.

1 (a) What problems does hot, dry weather bring?
  (b) How can these problems be overcome?

Look at 5D.

2 (a) What problems does very cold weather bring?
  (b) How can these problems be overcome?

Look at 5C and 5E.

3 (a) What problems does windy weather bring?
  (b) How can these problems be overcome?

4 What types of weather would stop these activities:
  (a) football match
  (b) tennis match
  (c) sailing
  (d) skiing?

Look at 5B.

5 What name is given to putting extra water on the land?

Look at 5C.

6 What weather problems do greenhouses overcome for the farmer?

Look at 5D and 5E.

7 How can driving in windy and snowy weather be made safer?

F Questions

CASE STUDY OF SOUTH-EAST ENGLAND, 1987

Look at Figure 5.5.

F1 Were the temperatures in south-east England in 1987 above or below average?

F2 Was the total rainfall above or below average?

F3 Was the amount of sunshine above or below average?

Look at Figure 5.6.

F4 Describe the problems faced by drivers during the cold spell in January.

F5 Who would have enjoyed this cold spell more: children or senior citizens? Give reasons for your answer.

Look at Figure 5.7.

F6 Do you think everyone enjoyed the long spell of hot dry weather in July? Give reasons for your answer.

Figure 5.1 Crop land being irrigated

**Final Week of Wimbledon '87
29 June–4 July**

**3rd Test Match
England v Pakistan
2–7 July 1987**

Figure 5.2

F7 In what ways would the events on the previous page have been affected by the weather?

Look at Figure 5.12.

F8 In what ways did the October storm affect (a) people at home and (b) people at sea?

G Questions

CASE STUDY OF SOUTH-EAST ENGLAND, 1987

Look at Figure 5.9.

G1 Compare the temperatures in 1987 with the average.

Look at Figure 5.6.

G2 In what ways would the cold spell have affected outdoor sports?

G3 People were warned about the cold spell by forecasters. Do you think this helped them very much? Give reasons for your answer.

Look at Figure 5.7.

G4 Describe how the hot dry weather in July would have helped some groups of workers but caused problems to others.

Figure 5.3	
Rainfall in South-east England (Gatwick) 1987	
Month	**Rainfall (mm)**
March	77
April	84
May	2
June	81
July	16
August	28

Look at Figure 5.3.

G5 Wheat is a popular crop in south-east England. It needs 50–90 mm of rain each month from March to August to grow best. Was 1987 a good year for growing wheat? Give reasons for your answer.

Look at Figure 5.12.

G6 In what ways would people travelling in south-east England have been affected by the October storm?

Look at Figure 5.13.

G7 Do you think farmers in south-east England prefer high pressure or low pressure conditions in winter?

CASE STUDY OF SOUTH-EAST ENGLAND, 1987

Figure 5.4

Introduction

South-east England includes the counties of Kent, Surrey, West and East Sussex and London south of the River Thames. Most people in this area live in London but there are also thousands of commuters who live in towns and villages and travel to London each day to work.

South-east England is an area of forested ridges and grassy chalk hills, grazed by sheep. Between the hills are fertile river valleys in which fruit, vegetables and cereals are grown. The coast is popular with tourists, as well as with people taking the ferries or Channel Tunnel to Europe. The people here are all affected by the weather in their daily lives and 1987 is a year most of them will remember for a long time.

Figure 5.5

London's Weather, 1987

	1987	Average
Average temperature (°C)	10.2	1.5
Total rainfall (mm)	685	620
Total sunshine (hours)	1616	1556

Figure 5.6

The coldest weather of the whole year was in January when there were frosts on 14 successive nights, between the 7th and 20th, and on the 12th the **maximum** temperature was −6°C. Fog was common in low-lying areas and there were some quite heavy falls of snow. Figure 5.6 shows a weather map for one of the days during that cold spell.

Figure 5.7

As well as being the coldest month, January was also the driest month of the year. The driest spell, however, occurred in summer. Between 28 June and 13 July, no rain fell in most parts of south-east England and temperatures reached over 20°C every day.

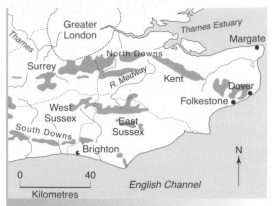

Figure 5.8 Location map of south-east England

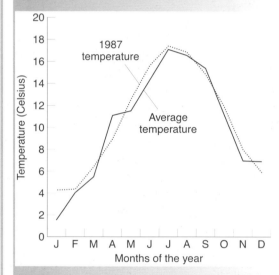

Figure 5.9 Temperatures in London, 1987

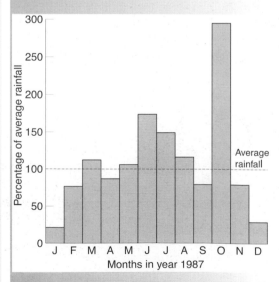

Figure 5.10 Rainfall in London, 1987

Figure 5.11

August saw the hottest day of the whole year (27°C in London). It was also one of the wettest days, as thunderstorms occurred and were followed over the next few days by a succession of depressions.

Figure 5.12

The wettest month was October and much of the rain in this month fell in what has come to be known as the storm of the century.

On the night of October 15, 1987 a severe depression moved across southern England. As it moved, conditions worsened and the winds became stronger until they reached 100 km/h in the early hours of October 16.

As it swept across the country the storm left a trail of havoc resembling a battlefield in its wake. Nineteen people died on the night and 11 more deaths followed in the next few days. About one building in six suffered substantial damage, especially to roofs, walls, chimneys and windows, and many homes were completely destroyed. One family living on the 10th floor of an 18-storey block of flats in London awoke to see the outside wall of their bedroom disappearing as the winds tore away the walls and windows of the poorly built flats.

The total repair bill for buildings was £1.6 billion and the storm cost insurance companies £2 million in claims. Fifteen million trees were blown down as the storm unleashed its power, including one-third of all the trees in Kew Gardens. Power lines were pulled down, causing loss of electricity for several days in some areas. A ferry was blown ashore at Folkestone and many coastal piers suffered serious damage.

Figure 5.13

The end of 1987 saw high pressure systems dominate the weather in south-east England and December was the second driest month of the year with only 15 mm of rain falling in London. Maximum temperatures were very high for the time of year, reaching 15°C on December 29, hotter than some of the days in summer.

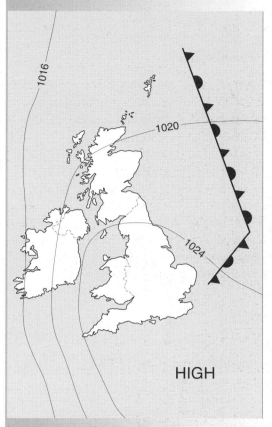

Figure 5.14 A typical weather map during a cold winter spell

Figure 5.15 Car crushed by a tree during the Great Storm

45

Extension Text

5F THE WEATHER AND FARMING

Although everyone is affected by the weather, farmers are affected more than anyone else.

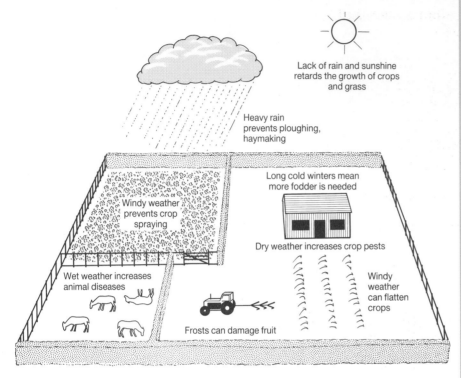

Lack of rain and sunshine retards the growth of crops and grass

Heavy rain prevents ploughing, haymaking

Long cold winters mean more fodder is needed

Windy weather prevents crop spraying

Dry weather increases crop pests

Wet weather increases animal diseases

Windy weather can flatten crops

Frosts can damage fruit

Figure 5.16 The effects of the weather on farmers

5G THE WEATHER AND SOIL EROSION

The weather affects the health of the farmer's crops and animals, as well as the jobs that can be done on the farm. It also affects the soil. Soil can be eroded by wind or rain, but it is only eroded when there is no vegetation to protect it.

Wind erosion takes place:
- if the soil is unprotected
- where the land is flat
- in dry weather

Rain erosion takes place:
- if the soil is unprotected
- where the land is sloping
- during heavy rain

To reduce wind erosion, lines of trees called **shelter belts** can be used. These slow down the speed of the wind. Irrigation also helps by making the soil more moist and less easy for the wind to pick up.

To reduce rain erosion, farmers plough across slopes along the contours. This is called **contour ploughing**. The furrows made by the ploughshares trap water therefore less runs downhill.

Slopes can also be **terraced** – made into steps. This slows down the speed of the run-off down the slope.

ⓔ Questions

Read the Extension Text.

ⓔ1 Describe some farming problems caused by
   (a) heavy rain
   (b) very cold weather
   (c) windy weather.

ⓔ2 What conditions are necessary for (a) wind erosion and
   (b) rain erosion of the soil to take place?

Figure 5.17 Contour ploughing

ⓔ3 Explain how contour ploughing reduces soil erosion.

ⓒ Questions

CASE STUDY OF SOUTH-EAST ENGLAND, 1987

Look at Figure 5.10.

ⓒ1 Compare the rainfall in London in 1987 with the average.

Look at Figure 5.6.

ⓒ2 Describe the advantages and disadvantages of the cold spell in January to the local people.

Look at Figure 5.11.

ⓒ3 Describe how summer outdoor sports (for example tennis, cricket and golf) are affected by the passage of a depression.

Look at Figure 5.12.

ⓒ4 In what ways would businesses have been affected by the October storm?

ⓒ5 The severity of the storm was not forecast by the Meteorological Office. People have disagreed over how useful an accurate forecast would have been to the local people. Describe the different arguments that could be put forward.

Look at Figure 5.13.

ⓒ6 Which will cause more soil erosion in south-east England in winter: high pressure or low pressure conditions? Give reasons for your answer.

UNIT ⑥

Skills in Climate Studies

Core Text

6A INTRODUCTION

It is important to study world climates in geography because, like the weather, they play a big part in shaping the physical and human landscape.

For the Standard Grade examination you need to know:
1 the characteristics of the equatorial, tundra, tropical desert and Mediterranean climates,
2 the location of these climates throughout the world,
3 how to identify these climates from climate graphs and tables, and
4 the ways in which climates affect people and their activities.

You also need to develop the following enquiry skills:
1 how to process climate statistics by drawing climate graphs, and
2 how to analyse climate information.

The rest of this unit deals with ways of processing climate information.

6B PROCESSING INFORMATION

Most information gathered about climate is in number form, such as temperature, rainfall and sunshine figures for different months of the year. Although these figures are sometimes shown in the form of tables, it is more usual and clearer to process them into graphs.

6C DRAWING A CLIMATE GRAPH

A climate graph is a comparison graph. It compares the temperature and rainfall at one place in each month of the year. The two graphs are drawn with two different vertical axes. This is how to draw a climate graph:
- start by drawing x (horizontal) and y (vertical) axes in pencil
- choose a suitable scale for the x axis, which is used to show the months of the year
- drawn another vertical axis down the right-hand side of your graph, as shown in Figure 6.1

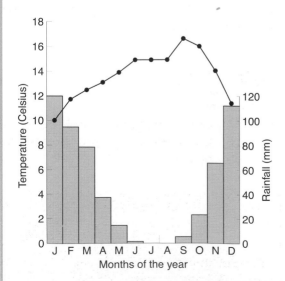

Figure 6.1 The climate of San Francisco, USA

- work out a suitable scale for temperature on the left-hand vertical axis
- work out a suitable scale for rainfall on the right-hand vertical axis
- in pencil, draw a bar graph to show the rainfall, making sure the 'bars' are not so tall that they will completely cover the temperature graph
- shade in the rainfall graph lightly
- in pencil, draw a line graph to show the temperature, making sure you place a cross or dot for each month in the middle of that month's column (see Figure 6.1)
- once you have checked it, go over all the pencil lines in ink
- label all the axes and give the graph a title

6D DRAWING A SCATTER GRAPH

A scatter graph is used to show a possible relationship (or connection) between two sets of amounts. This is how to draw a scatter graph

- draw x (horizontal) and y (vertical) axes in pencil
- use the x axis to show the information that is either distance or time (for example in Figure 6.2 the x axis shows height above sea-level)
- use the y axis to show the information that is an amount or frequency (for example in Figure 6.2 the y axis shows the rainfall total)
- find out the highest numbers required on the x and y axes and work out a suitable scale for each axis
- plot each point carefully in pencil with a small cross or dot (note that on a scatter graph the dots are not joined with a line but are left scattered over the graph)
- when you have finished and checked your graph, go over all the lines and dots in ink
- label the axes clearly and give the graph a title

Once the scatter graph is finished, you will be able to look at the pattern of crosses and identify any relationship between the two sets of data (for example Figure 6.2 shows that rainfall generally increases with height in the Fort William area).

Ⓕ Questions

Look at 6C.

Ⓕ1 (a) Copy the climate graph in Figure 6.3.
  (b) Complete the graph using the information in the table below.

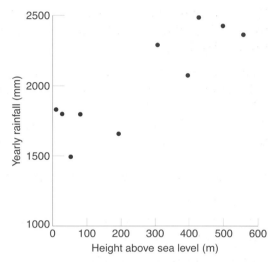

Figure 6.2 The connection between rainfall and height in the Fort William area

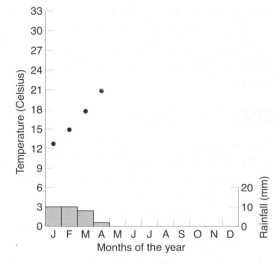

Figure 6.3 The climate of Yuma, USA

The climate of Yuma, USA

	J	F	M	A	M	J	J	A	S	O	N	D
Temperature (°C)	13	15	18	21	25	30	33	33	30	23	17	13
Rainfall (mm)	10	10	8	2	0	0	5	15	10	8	5	13

Look at 6D.

F2 (a) Copy the scatter graph in Figure 6.4.

(b) Complete the graph by adding the information for May to December shown in the table below.

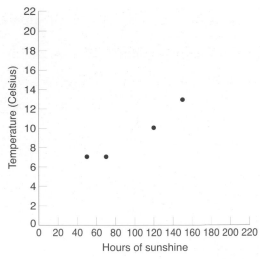

Figure 6.4 The connection between temperature and sunshine in London

Figure 6.5

The climate of London

	Average maximum temperature (°C)	Sunshine (hours)
January	7	50
February	7	70
March	10	120
April	13	150
May	17	200
June	20	210
July	22	200
August	21	180
September	19	150
October	15	110
November	10	70
December	8	50

Look at the tables below and on page 51.

F3 Which table of information, Figure 6.6 or 6.7, is better shown by a scatter graph?

Figure 6.6

Average temperatures at different latitudes

Location	Average temperature (°C)	Distance from the Equator (°)
Singapore	27	1
In Salah	25	27
Lima	20	12
Gibraltar	19	36
Perth	18	32
Victoria	10	48
Boston	9	42
Utrecht	9	52
Yakutsk	−14	62
Bulun	−15	71

Figure 6.7

Temperatures in Madrid

Month	Average temperature (°C)
January	6
February	7
March	10
April	13
May	16
June	21
July	24
August	24
September	20
October	15
November	9
December	6

Figure 6.8

Temperatures in Antarctica

Year	Average temperature (°C)
1950	−6
1955	−3
1960	−7
1965	−4
1970	−4
1975	−5
1980	−6
1985	−4
1990	−3
1995	−2

G Questions

Look at 6C.

G1 Using the information in the table below, draw a climate graph for Kiev.

The climate of Kiev, Ukraine

	J	F	M	A	M	J	J	A	S	O	N	D
Temperature (°C)	−6	−5	0	7	15	19	20	19	14	8	1	−4
Rainfall (mm)		33	25	41	43	48	66	79	58	46	46	38	38

Look at 6D.

G2 Using the information in the table below, draw a scatter graph to show the relationship between temperature and height in the Fort William area.

Temperatures in the Fort William area

Average temp. (°C)	Height (m)
5.0	503
7.0	305
8.5	4
7.5	198
8.0	61
5.0	564
9.0	30
7.5	91

G3 Which table of information (Figure 6.6 or 6.7 – see **F** Questions) is better shown by a scatter graph? Give a reason for your answer.

Questions

Look at 6C.

C1 Using the information in the table below draw the climate graph for Shenyang.

The climate of Shenyang, China

	J	F	M	A	M	J	J	A	S	O	N	D
Temperature (°C)	−12	−8	0	10	17	23	26	25	18	9	−1	−9
Rainfall (mm)	8	8	18	28	69	84	183	170	64	36	28	15

Look at 6D.

C2 Using the information in the table below draw a scatter graph to show the relationship between temperature range and distance from the sea.

Temperature ranges around Europe

Location	Annual temperature range (°C)	Distance from the sea (km)
Santander	9	1
Cherbourg	11	2
Birmingham	12	107
Paris	15	180
Brussels	16	100
Hamburg	18	80
Madrid	18	325
Lyon	19	275
Munich	21	300
Vienna	23	350
Warsaw	23	275
Bucharest	27	200

C3 Which table of information (Figure 6.6, 6.7 or 6.8 – see **F** Questions) would be best shown by a scatter graph? Justify your answer.

UNIT ⑦

Climates with Rain all Year

Core Text

7A WEATHER AND CLIMATE

The **weather** is made up of different elements, such as temperature, rainfall and wind speed. It changes from day to day and from hour to hour.

The **climate** is the weather we usually get, for example cool, wet winters and warm summers, worked out over many years (usually 30) as an average.

7B CLIMATE REGIONS

Figure 7.1 shows the climate of Edinburgh. Other places in Britain have a similar climate – they all have warm summers, cool winters and rain in every month. All of Britain therefore belongs to the same **climate region**. A climate region is an area in which all the places have a similar climate.

There are many climate regions in the world. Some, like ours, have rain in every month, some only have rain in a few months of the year and some hardly get any rain at all. The rest of this unit looks at two climates that have rain in every month.

7C REASONS FOR DIFFERENT CLIMATES

There are several reasons why different climates occur:
* **latitude**   generally, places near the Equator are hot and places near the poles are cold
* **height**   places higher up are colder and wetter
* **nearness to oceans**   places near oceans are mild in summer and winter and rainy all year; places far from oceans are drier and have more extreme temperatures.

7D EQUATORIAL CLIMATE: LOCATION

Figure 7.2 (overleaf) shows the location of the equatorial climate. It is found in lowland areas near the Equator. It includes the vast Amazon River Basin in South America, the Congo River Basin in Africa and small areas in South-east Asia and the islands of Malaysia and Indonesia.

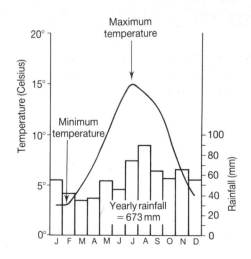

Figure 7.1 The climate of Edinburgh

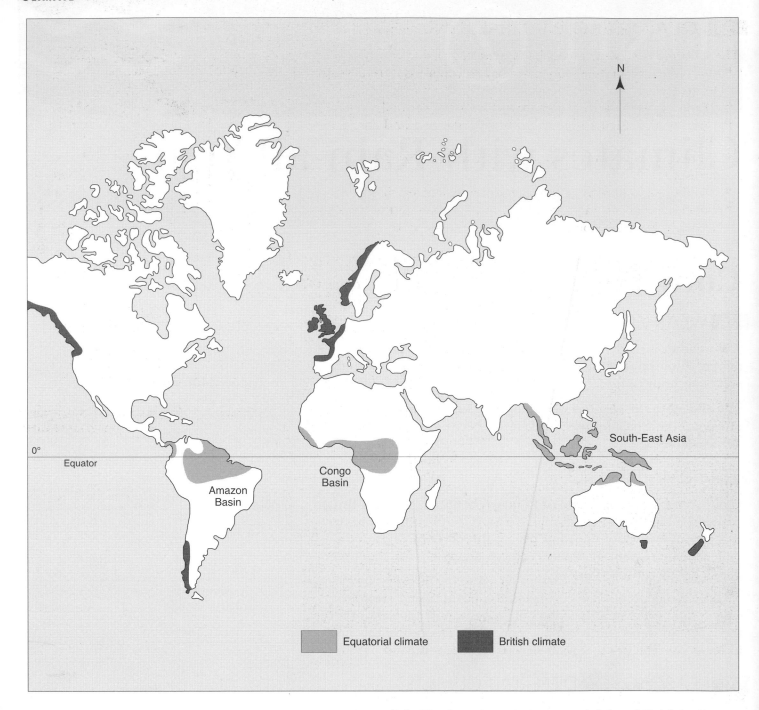

Figure 7.2 The location of the equatorial and British climates

7E EQUATORIAL CLIMATE: CHARACTERISTICS

The characteristics of the equatorial climate are:
- maximum temperatures are high, approximately 27°C
- minimum temperatures are also high, approximately 25°C
- temperatures do not vary much from month to month and there are no seasons
- a lot of rain falls in every month
- annual rainfall total is high, at least 1500 mm.

7F EQUATORIAL CLIMATE: ADVANTAGES

The advantages of the equatorial climate are:

- the high temperatures and rainfall allow many different crops to grow
- food crops such as rice, cassava and maize grow well
- cash crops such as bananas, rubber, pineapples and cocoa also thrive
- there are many rivers in these areas, which are used for transport
- the rivers can also be used to generate hydroelectric power
- the climate allows rainforest to grow and many of the trees are valuable for their wood, for example teak and mahogany.

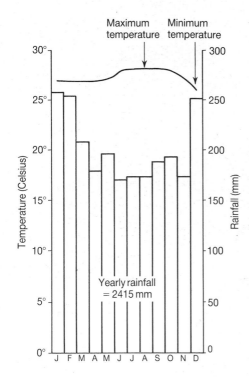

Figure 7.3 The climate of Singapore: an equatorial climate

Figure 7.4 The Tucurui hydroelectric power station in the Amazon rainforest

7G EQUATORIAL CLIMATE: DISADVANTAGES

The disadvantages of the equatorial climate are:

- the dense rainforest makes it difficult to build roads and railways so the people in these areas are cut off from the rest of the world
- because they are cut off the people have to grow crops and rear animals to feed themselves; such people are called **subsistence farmers**
- the heavy rain makes the soil poor and difficult to farm well
- because the soil is poor, until recently most people farmed a small area of land for a few years and then moved to another area of forest where they would clear the trees, burn them, grow crops such as cassava, yams and rice, and then move again when the crops began to grow badly; this type of farming is called **shifting cultivation** (see Figure 7.5).

Figure 7.5 Shifting cultivation in Ecuador

Core Questions

Look at 7A.

1 What is meant by the 'climate' of an area?

Look at 7C.

2 Why are some places colder than others?

3 Why are some places wetter than others?

4 Copy the table below. Use Figures 7.1 and 7.3 to complete it.

	Equatorial climate	British climate
Maximum temperature (°C)		
Minimum temperature (°C)		
Yearly rainfall (mm)		

5 How do you know that the climate graph in Figure 7.6 shows an equatorial climate?

Look at 7F.

6 In what ways are the rivers in rainforests useful?

Look at 7G.

7 In what ways do dense rainforest and poor soils affect people?

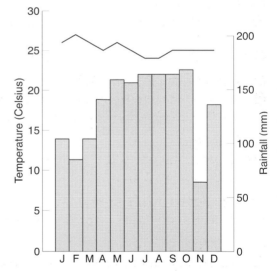

Figure 7.6 A climate graph

  Questions

CASE STUDY OF THE CAMEROON REPUBLIC

Look at Figure 7.7.

F1 Which area of Cameroon has an equatorial climate?

Look at Figure 7.9.

F2 Do the temperatures in Douala change much from month to month?

F3 Does the rainfall in Douala change much from month to month?

Look at Figure 7.10.

F4 Are the temperatures in Dschang typical of an equatorial climate?

F5 Is the rainfall in Dschang typical of an equatorial climate?

Look at Figure 7.11.

F6 Do you think the equatorial area of Cameroon is good for farming? Give reasons for your answer.

Look at Figure 7.14.

F7 In what ways does the rainfall affect the crops grown in Cameroon?

Look at Figure 7.16.

F8 In what ways are the rivers useful to the people of Cameroon?

Look at Figure 7.17.

F9 Do you think many tourists will visit Korup National Park?

G Questions

CASE STUDY OF THE CAMEROON REPUBLIC

Look at Figure 7.9.

G1 Describe the changes in temperature during the year in Douala.

G2 Describe the changes in rainfall during the year in Douala.

Look at Figures 7.9 and 7.10.

G3 Which is the better example of an equatorial climate: Douala or Dschang? Give reasons for your answer.

Look at Figure 7.14.

G4 In what ways does the total rainfall affect the crops grown in the equatorial area of Cameroon?

Look at Figures 7.11 and 7.12.

G5 Describe the farming problems caused by the climate.

Look at Figure 7.16.

G6 Rivers in Cameroon have many uses. What do you think is the most important use of the rivers to the people of Cameroon? Give reasons for your answer.

Look at Figure 7.17.

G7 Was it a good idea to make the Korup Rainforest into a National Park? Give reasons for your answer.

CASE STUDY OF THE CAMEROON REPUBLIC

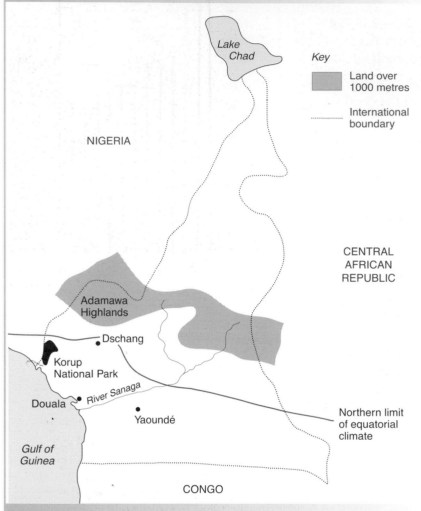

Figure 7.7 The location of the Cameroon Republic

Figure 7.8

Introduction

The Cameroon Republic is on the west coast of Central Africa. It lies just north of the Equator and the south and the west of the country, along the coast, have an equatorial climate. Inland are mountains and, in the north, grassland areas.

Most people live by farming – coffee and cocoa are the chief crops. In the north, cattle rearing is more important.

French Cameroon became independent in 1960 and united with the former British Cameroon in 1961. Cameroon has a population of 13 million people and its capital is Yaoundé.

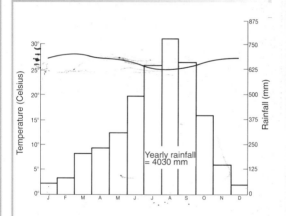

Figure 7.9 The climate of Douala, Cameroon

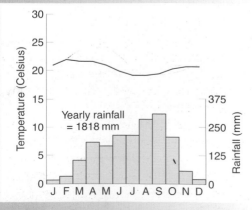

Figure 7.10 The climate of Dschang, Cameroon

Figure 7.11

Shifting Cultivation in Cameroon

The humid equatorial climate in west Cameroon allows a variety of crops to be grown. These include food crops, such as cassava, cocoyams and maize, and export crops, such as cocoa, bananas, rubber and palm oil.

The rainfall here is very heavy and so, once the trees are cut down, the soils quickly become infertile. Because of this many farmers here practise shifting cultivation. They move to a new area when their land becomes too poor for growing crops and they do not return there for many years, by which time the vegetation has regrown and the soil has become fertile again. For this type of farming, each family needs a large area of forest.

Because the population of Cameroon is growing, the area of land for each family is being reduced and many people have now given up shifting cultivation and practise **bush fallowing** instead. With this method the people stay in the same place but they only cultivate a few of their fields each year. The rest is left fallow, to allow the soil to become fertile again. Instead of each field being used for a different crop, many crops are grown in the same field at the same time. This is called **intercropping**. This prevents soil erosion as the soil is never bare and will not be washed away by the heavy rains. It also reduces the chance of disease affecting the crops.

Figure 7.13 The rainforest in Cameroon

Figure 7.12

Plantation Farming in Cameroon

Most of the export crops are grown on large estates called **plantations**. Each plantation specialises in one export crop only, and they are usually found near the coast or beside railway lines so that the crops can be exported easily.

A typical plantation is owned by a multi-national company, covers about 5000 hectares and provides housing, schools and hospitals for its workers. The company might also build a road or railway track.

Plantation farming provides over half of Cameroon's exports and employs thousands of workers. The price of the crops, however, fluctuates greatly from year to year and, although the rainfall is reliable here, there is always the risk of disease wiping out the crop or of tornadoes, which can flatten crops and trees.

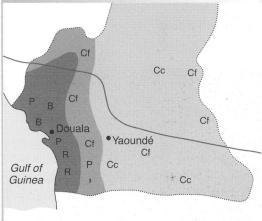

Key

■ Over 2500 mm rainfall	B bananas
▨ 2000–2500 mm rainfall	Cc cocoa
□ 1500–2000 mm rainfall	Cf coffee
	P oil palm
	R rubber

— Northern limit of equatorial climate

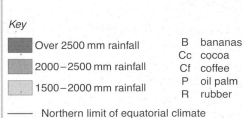

Figure 7.14 Rainfall and cash crops in Cameroon

Figure 7.15

Timber in Cameroon

Along the coast of Cameroon are mangrove forests while inland, in the south, there is still much rainforest. Some of the trees are cut down and sold, especially along the coast where the communications are better and electricity is available. Inland, the remoteness restricts development. Only a small number of trees are valuable and the industry requires a large capital investment. Timber at present accounts for four per cent of Cameroon's exports.

Figure 7.16

Water Resources in Cameroon

There are many rivers in equatorial Cameroon, which are used to transport logs and farm produce to the coast, from where they can be exported. Although slow, this is a cheap form of transport and is especially useful since there are so few roads and railways. Waterfalls on the Sanaga River have been used to make hydroelectricity. This has attracted a limited number of industries, such as aluminium smelting, which employ a few thousand workers. A shortage of raw materials and skilled labour has restricted further economic development. The rivers provide plenty of fish which is an important source of protein for the local people.

Figure 7.17

The Korup Rainforest

The Korup Rainforest is in west Cameroon on the border with Nigeria and is one of the most difficult areas in the country to reach and penetrate. It was made a National Park in 1986 in order to protect the forest and its wildlife. Over 400 species of trees, 250 bird species and 140 types of fish are found here; some of them are very rare. No one lives in the National Park itself, which is used only for research. Scientists studying the trees and plants here have found 90 different chemicals, which can be used in industry and medicine. It is hoped to attract tourists to the National Park and local people will be employed as guides.

 People from six villages have been moved from the park to more fertile areas just outside, where they are encouraged to practice traditional farming methods, such as hunting and shifting cultivation, and other activities that do not destroy the rainforest environment.

Extension Text

7H BRITISH CLIMATE: LOCATION

Figure 7.2 shows the location of the British climate. It is not confined to Britain and north-west Europe. Other areas in the world with a similar latitude and on the west coast of continents experience the same mild, wet conditions brought by onshore winds from the west.

As Figure 7.18 shows, however, there are differences in temperature and, especially, rainfall within this region. Rainfall varies with height and with distance from the west coast (the source of the rain-bearing winds). Temperatures also vary with latitude and height. The **annual temperature range** (the difference between the maximum and minimum temperatures) increases with distance from the west coast.

Figure 7.18

Location	Valdivia (Chile)	Emden (Germany)	Shannon (Ireland)
	On west coast, with Andes Mountains behind	On north coast, in lowland area	On west coast, in lowland area
Latitude	40°S	53°N	53°N
Max. temp. (°C)	18	17	16
Min. temp. (°C)	9	1	5
Temp. range (°C)	9	16	11
Annual rainfall (mm)	2490	740	930

7J BRITISH CLIMATE: ADVANTAGES

The advantages of the British climate are:
- it is reliable: there are few droughts and few long cold spells
- there are plentiful rivers
- water can be transferred to drier areas
- hydroelectricity is an important source of power
- the wet climate encourages the growth of grass, so livestock farming is important.

7K BRITISH CLIMATE: DISADVANTAGES

The disadvantages of the British climate are:
- the cloudy weather restricts crop growth
- the cloudy, wet weather deters tourists
- grass stops growing in the cool winters so farm animals need to be given extra food
- rain washes minerals out of the topsoil (called **leaching**) so farmers need to improve the soil.

E Questions

Read the Extension Text.

E1 What is meant by the annual temperature range?

E2 Which areas of the world have a British climate?

E3 Why do places with a British climate have different rainfall totals?

Look at Figures 7.1 and 7.3.

E4 What is the annual temperature range in
(a) Edinburgh and
(b) Singapore?

C Questions

CASE STUDY OF THE CAMEROON REPUBLIC

Look at Figure 7.10.

C1 Describe the characteristics of the climate of Dschang.

Look at Figure 7.9.

C2 Do you agree with the statement below? Give reasons for your answer.
'Douala has a typical equatorial climate'

Look at Figure 7.11.

C3 In what ways have farming methods in Cameroon adapted to the equatorial climate?

Look at Figures 7.12, 7.15 and 7.16.

C4 The natural environment of Cameroon provides fast-flowing rivers, plentiful timber and many valuable crops, Which of these will be most useful to the country's development? Give reasons for your answer.

Look at Figure 7.17.

C5 Describe the advantages and disadvantages of the Korup National Park for tourism.

UNIT ⑧

Climates with a Dry Season

Core Text

8A MEDITERRANEAN CLIMATE: LOCATION

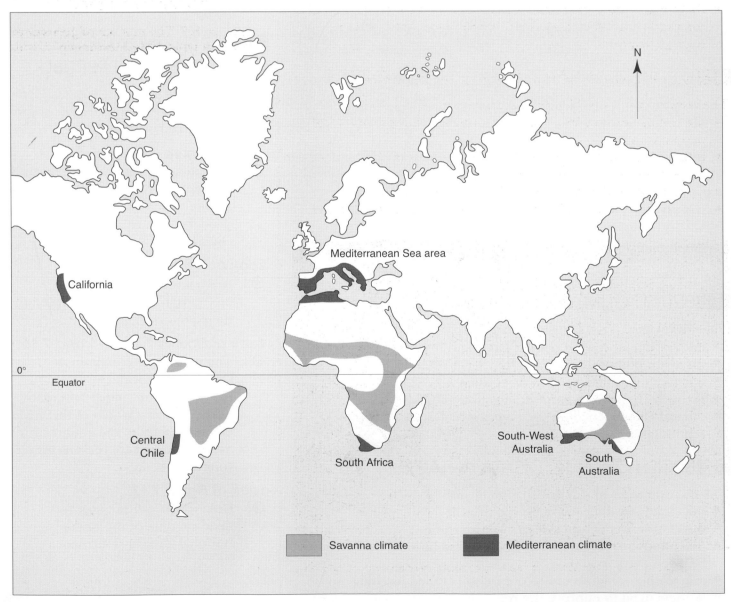

Figure 8.1 The location of the Mediterranean and Savanna climates

Figure 8.1 shows areas with a Mediterranean climate. They are found next to places with a British climate but are nearer the Equator. They include countries around the Mediterranean Sea, such as Italy and Greece, together with parts of Australia, South Africa, Chile and the state of California in the USA.

Many people live in this climatic region and it contains cities such as Barcelona in Spain, Marseilles in France, Melbourne in Australia, Cape Town in South Africa and Los Angeles and San Francisco in the USA.

8B MEDITERRANEAN CLIMATE: CHARACTERISTICS

The characteristics of the Mediterranean climate are:
- the maximum temperature is high in summer, between 22 and 28°C
- the minimum temperature in winter is mild, approximately 10°C
- there is very little or no rain in the summer months (a **drought**)
- the yearly rainfall varies from place to place, but is usually less than 1000 mm.

8C MEDITERRANEAN CLIMATE: ADVANTAGES

The advantages of the Mediterranean climate are:
- the hot dry sunny summers attract tourists, who provide local people with jobs
- if there is enough water, the hot sunny summers allow many crops to grow, for example citrus fruits
- winters are mild and wet enough for crops to grow
- solar power can be widely used because of the sunny summers.

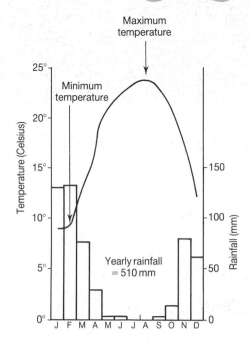

Figure 8.2 **The climate of Jerusalem, Israel: a typical Mediterranean climate**

Figure 8.3 **The Mediterranean climate attracts many tourists**

8D MEDITERRANEAN CLIMATE: DISADVANTAGES

The disadvantages of the Mediterranean climate are:
- in summer the vegetation is so dry that fires break out and spread quickly
- it is unsuitable for cattle rearing, as grass does not grow well
- strong winds and occasional cold winds can damage crops so farmers plant **shelter belts** of trees to protect them
- reservoirs have to be built to store water for use during the dry summers
- in order to grow crops in summer, farmers have to **irrigate** their fields (put extra water on to them), which can be expensive.

Figure 8.5 Small-scale irrigation schemes: simple water-lifting devices are cheap, but they do not provide much water for crops and are not very reliable

Figure 8.4 Large-scale irrigation schemes: expensive concrete dams hold back huge reservoirs of water, which can be pumped to areas many kilometres away

Core Questions

Look at Figure 8.6.

1 How do you know that the graph in Figure 8.6 is for a Mediterranean climate?

Look at 8B.

2 What is a drought?

Look at 8C.

3 Why does the Mediterranean climate attract many tourists?
4 Name two popular tourist areas with a Mediterranean climate.

Look at 8D.

5 Why do fires often break out in summer?
6 Why do some farmers need shelter belts?
7 What is meant by 'irrigation'?
8 Give an example of
  (a) a small-scale irrigation scheme and
  (b) a large-scale irrigation scheme.

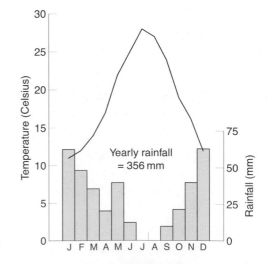

Figure 8.6 A Mediterranean climate

F Questions

CASE STUDY OF GREECE

Look at Figure 8.12.

F1 Which is the wetter season in Athens: winter or summer?

F2 What is the temperature of the warmest month?

F3 What is the temperature of the coldest month?

F4 In which season do farmers need to irrigate their fields? Give a reason for your answer.

Look at Figure 8.11.

F5 Describe the problems that the heavy rains bring to farmers in Greece.

Look at Figure 8.14.

F6 Which is the better method of irrigation in Greece: using windmills or building reservoirs? Give reasons for your answer.

Look at Figure 8.7.

F7 Do you agree with the statement below the photograph? Give a reason for your answer.

Look at Figures 8.15 and 8.16.

F8 The irrigated land in the coastal plains is used differently from the hillsides nearby. What are the main differences?

Figure 8.7 The people in Greece have the perfect climate in which to live

G Questions

CASE STUDY OF GREECE

Look at Figure 8.12.

G1 Describe the rainfall pattern throughout the year in Athens.

Look at Figure 8.18.

G2 Describe the attractions of the climate for all year round tourism in Greece.

Look at Figure 8.11.

G3 In which season does the climate pose more problems to Greek farmers: winter or summer? Explain your answer.

Look at Figure 8.15.

G4 Give one argument for and one argument against planting more trees in the mountains of Greece.

Look at Figures 8.13 and 8.14.

G5 Describe the ways in which Greek farmers cope with the long, dry season.

Look at Figures 8.10 and 8.14.

G6 Do you agree with the statement below? Explain your answer. 'Greece could have far more large irrigation schemes, using dams across rivers'

Look at Figures 8.15 and 8.16.

G7 Compare the land uses in the coastal plains with those in the surrounding hillsides.

Figure 8.8 Terraces to reduce soil erosion

CASE STUDY OF GREECE

Figure 8.9

Introduction

Greece is a small country on the Mediterranean Sea in south-east Europe. One-fifth of the country is made up of islands, the largest of which is Crete. Even on the mainland nowhere is more than 130 km from the sea. The mainland is quite mountainous but along the coastal plains are found large cities, including the capital, Athens. Everywhere in Greece, except the highest parts, has a Mediterranean climate.

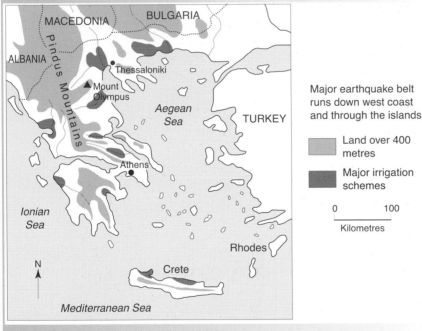

Major earthquake belt runs down west coast and through the islands

Land over 400 metres

Major irrigation schemes

0 ——— 100
Kilometres

Figure 8.10 Main cities, relief features and irrigation schemes in Greece

Figure 8.11

Farming and the Climate

Twenty-three per cent of the workforce in Greece are farmers and for them the Mediterranean climate brings problems. This is one of the reasons why so many are leaving the land to move to cities or migrate overseas.

During the summer drought, fires can break out and few crops can be grown unless there is expensive irrigation. When the rains do come, they are sometimes so heavy that they wash the soil into nearby rivers. The rivers burst their banks and flood extensive areas of coastal plains, depositing infertile sands and gravels. They also leave swamps which, in the past, have attracted mosquitoes, which spread malaria.

Sunshine hours											
131	150	179	241	312	335	377	363	272	220	180	137

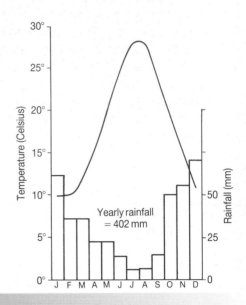

Yearly rainfall = 402 mm

Figure 8.12 The climate of Athens, Greece

Figure 8.13

Traditional Farming

In many parts of Greece, farming has changed little for centuries. Much of the farming is still subsistence farming, with people keeping animals and growing food for themselves. Sheep and goats are common as they can feed off the tough, wiry plants that survive the long dry season. They provide milk, butter and cheese. Wheat and barley grow during the winter and are harvested before the height of the summer. Vines and olives are found almost everywhere, their long roots helping them to find water in the hot dry climate. They also thrive in the poor soils here and provide the local people with fruit, wine and oil.

Figure 8.14

Irrigated Farming

Only about 10 per cent of the farmland is irrigated and small-scale schemes are the most common. Windmills are used to bring water up from underground to irrigate small areas of land. They are cheap to build and easy to use, although the water may sometimes dry up.

Large-scale schemes, shown in Figure 8.10, are less common as they are very expensive and there are few large rivers. The reservoirs also flood large areas of useful farmland. However, they do irrigate huge areas of land and they never run dry. Some are used to make hydroelectric power.

Figure 8.15

The Mountainous Interior

Mainland Greece is mountainous, the rugged limestone mountains rising to nearly 3000 metres at Mount Olympus. The mountains were once covered with trees but fires, goats and woodcutting have removed most of the forest. Bare soil has been washed away by rain, leaving deep gullies and barren land on which only a few shrubs and bushes grow (called **scrub** vegetation). Sheep and goats graze these areas in summer.

In attempts to stop soil erosion, people have cut steps or **terraces** into the hillsides. These provide extra flat land on which vines and olives now grow. The Greek government is trying to increase the area of forests in the uplands but the thin soils and dry climate make this difficult. The newly forested areas must be completely fenced off to prevent goats from eating the young saplings.

Figure 8.16

The Coastal Plains

The mountains of Greece reach to the sea and encircle small, isolated areas of coastal lowlands. Most of these coastal plains are found along the north and east coasts of the country. They are drained by rivers, which at one time flooded extensively, leaving large areas of swamps. The rivers are now being controlled, the swamps drained and the plains irrigated to allow commercial farming to take place. Vegetables, tobacco, rice, cotton and orchards of citrus fruits dominate these landscapes, which differ markedly from the upland areas that surround them. Figure 8.17 shows the ways in which the land is used across a typical irrigated coastal plain in Greece.

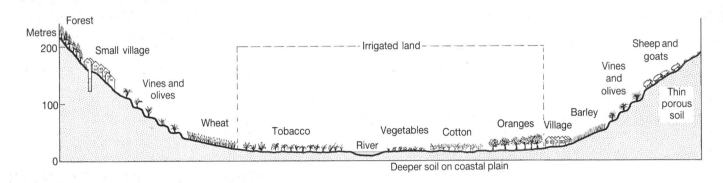

Figure 8.17 Land uses across a coastal plain in Greece

Figure 8.18

Tourism

Greece has been one of the most popular places for British holidaymakers since cheap package holidays started in the 1960s. The hot, dry, sunny summers and attractive scenery, especially on the islands, attract millions of visitors every summer. More recently, cheap winter package holidays have made Greece popular with north Europeans wanting to escape from long, cold winters and high heating bills.

Greece is also the cradle of Western civilisation and 5000 years of dramatic history have left a wealth of places of interest. These range from Minoan palaces, Mycenaean fortresses and classical temples to Crusader castles and Turkish Mosques, and they have attracted archaeologists, artists, geologists and classicists for hundreds of years.

Figure 8.19 The Acropolis

Extension Text

8E SAVANNA CLIMATE: LOCATION

Figure 8.1 shows the location of the Savanna or tropical wet and dry climate. It is found between the very rainy equatorial lands and the very dry hot deserts. Large areas of Africa and parts of South America and Australia have this climate.

8F SAVANNA CLIMATE: CHARACTERISTICS

The characteristics of the Savanna climate are:
- the maximum temperature is approximately 30°C
- the minimum temperature is approximately 20°C
- the annual temperature range is 10°C
- there is a winter drought, which lasts only one month near the equator but more than six months near the desert
- the annual rainfall varies from over 1000 mm near the equator to less than 500 mm near the desert
- rainfall is unreliable and some years are much wetter than others.

8G SAVANNA CLIMATE: ADVANTAGES

The advantages of the Savanna climate are:
- grass grows well and is suited to cattle farming
- crops also grow rapidly in the hot rainy season
- many food crops, for example maize and millet, and many cash crops, for example cotton, coffee and tea, can be grown
- winters are warm enough to allow two harvests a year
- the climate and wildlife attract tourists to safari parks, for example in Kenya and Tanzania.

8H SAVANNA CLIMATE: DISADVANTAGES

The disadvantages of the Savanna climate are:
- extra water is needed for the dry winters; this may come from rivers, wells or reservoirs, and people may need to spend many hours a day collecting water
- rivers and wells may run dry in the dry season and reservoirs are expensive to build
- it is necessary to irrigate fields if crops are to be grown during the winter
- rainfall may be below average for many years in succession, causing widespread famine, as happened in many parts of Africa, for example Ethiopia, in recent years
- in the drier areas the people have to be nomadic, moving from place to place to find water and grazing for their animals.

E Questions

Read the Extension Text.
E1 Which areas of the world have a Savanna climate?

E2 In what ways does the rainfall pattern in Savanna regions cause farmers problems?

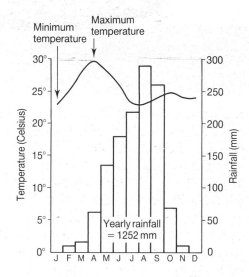

Figure 8.20 A typical Savanna climate

E3 How is the Savanna climate near the Equator different from the Savanna climate near the hot deserts?

E4 Describe some of the crops that thrive in a Savanna climate.

C Questions

CASE STUDY OF GREECE

Look at Figure 8.12.
C1 Compare the winter and summer climate of Athens.

Look at Figures 8.11 and 8.13–8.17.
C2 To what extent have farmers in Greece been able to overcome the problems brought about by the climate?

Look at Figure 8.10.
C3 Describe the distribution of large irrigation schemes in Greece.

C4 Describe the relationship between land use and the physical landscape in Figure 8.17.

Look at Figure 8.18.
C5 To what extent does the climate explain the popularity of Greece as a tourist area?

UNIT ⑨

Climates Dry all Year

Core Text

9A HOT DESERT CLIMATE: LOCATION

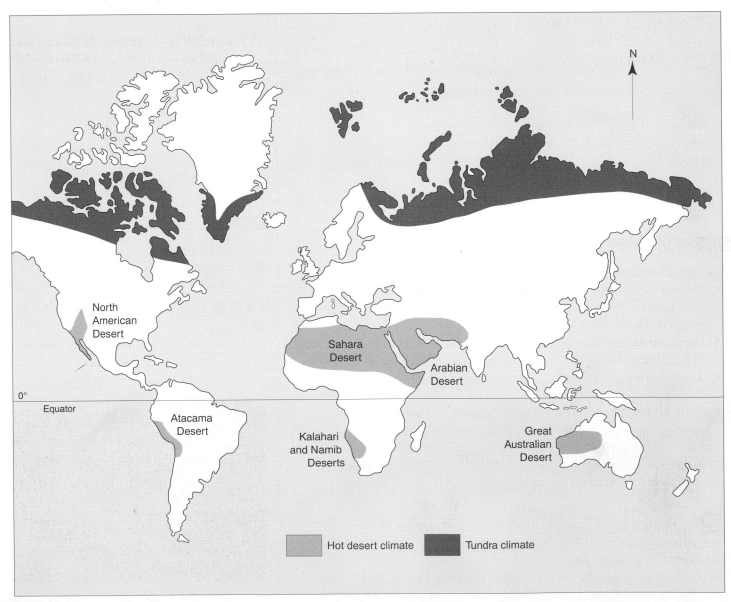

Figure 9.1 The location of the tundra and hot desert climates

Figure 9.1 shows the location of the world's hot deserts. They are found at the edge of the Tropics and on the western side of continents. The largest hot desert is the Sahara in north Africa and the only continent not to have a hot desert is Europe.

9B HOT DESERT CLIMATE: CHARACTERISTICS

The characteristics of a hot desert climate are:
- the maximum temperature reaches approximately 35°C
- the minimum temperature is approximately 12°C
- the yearly rainfall is less than 250 mm
- rain falls in only a few months, but often in torrential storms.

The hottest place in the world is Libya, in the Sahara Desert. Temperatures have reached 58°C here.

The driest area in the world is in Chile, in the Atacarma Desert. It only receives a few rainstorms every 100 years.

Figure 9.3

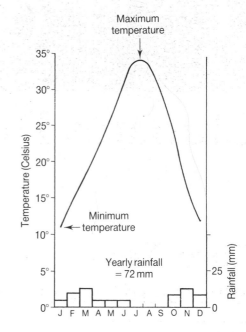

Figure 9.2 The climate of Touggourt, Algeria: a typical hot desert climate

9C HOT DESERT CLIMATE: ADVANTAGES

The advantages of the hot desert climate are:
- the very hot sunny climate and unusual scenery attracts tourists, for example to California, Egypt, Australia, especially at 'cooler' times of the year.
- if irrigation is possible, then a wide variety of crops will grow well in the hot sunny climate and two or three harvests a year are possible.

9D HOT DESERT CLIMATE: DISADVANTAGES

The disadvantages of the hot desert climate are:
- it is too dry to grow crops without irrigation
- in order to rear animals, such as camels, goats and sheep, the people have to be nomadic, moving from place to place in search of water and grazing
- farmers use small-scale irrigation schemes to get water from rivers or wells but these schemes provide little water and the river or well may run dry
- to obtain a large amount of water people have to build very expensive dams and reservoirs across major rivers, such as the Nile, Colorado and Indus.

Figure 9.4 The Grand Canyon in the North American Desert

Figure 9.5 Nomads near Timbuktu in the Sahara Desert

9E TUNDRA CLIMATE: LOCATION

Figure 9.1 shows the location of areas with a tundra climate. They are found near to the North Pole, mostly in northern Canada and Russia.

9F TUNDRA CLIMATE: CHARACTERISTICS

The characteristics of the tundra climate are:
- maximum temperatures no higher than 10°C
- minimum temperatures of −20°C or lower
- very low yearly rainfall total, usually less than 250 mm (a **cold desert**)
- a little rain or snow in every month.

The coldest inhabited town in the world is Olmyaken, in Russia, where temperatures have reached as low as −71°C

Figure 9.7

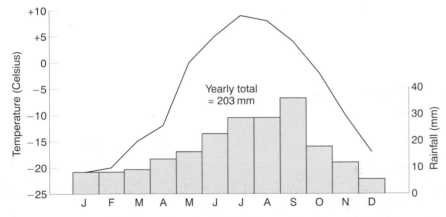

Yearly total = 203 mm

Figure 9.6 The climate of Hebron, Canada: a typical tundra climate

9G TUNDRA CLIMATE: ADVANTAGES

The advantages of the tundra climate are:
- summer days are long: on at least one day a year, inside the Arctic Circle, the sun does not set
- because it is so cold, there are fewer bacteria, viruses and flies to spread disease
- a variety of animals that can be hunted for their meat and fur, for example polar bears, seals, beavers and reindeer, live in this climate.

9H TUNDRA CLIMATE: DISADVANTAGES

The disadvantages of the tundra climate are:

- it is too cold to grow crops so food has to be brought in, which is expensive
- people who make a living by hunting and herding animals (for example the Lapps of north Norway) have to be nomadic in order to find fresh grazing for their animals
- in winter there is at least one day inside the Arctic Circle when the sun does not rise
- just below the surface the soil is permanently frozen (called **permafrost**); this causes many problems
- the climate also makes living conditions very difficult.

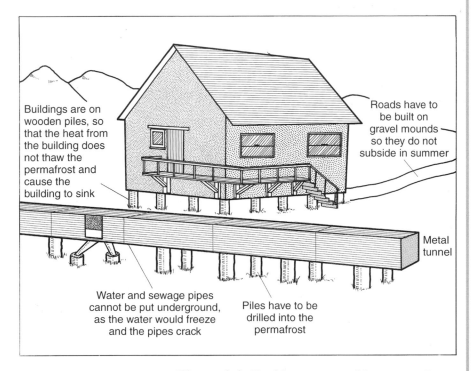

Figure 9.8 Problems caused by permafrost

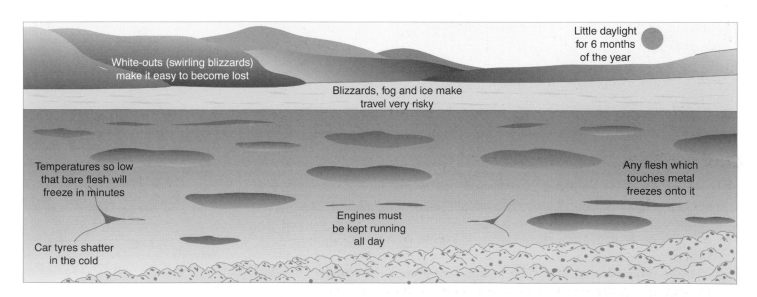

Figure 9.9 Problems caused by the climate

Core Questions

1 Copy the table below and use Figures 9.2 and 9.6 to complete it.

	Hot deserts	Tundra climate
Maximum temperature		
Minimum temperature		
Yearly rainfall		

Look at 9C.
2 Why do hot deserts attract tourists?
3 What are the advantages of hot deserts for growing crops?

Look at 9D.
4 Why are many people in hot deserts nomads?

Look at 9H.
5 What is permafrost?

Look at Figure 9.8.
6 Why do roads in the tundra have to be built on gravel?
7 Why are buildings on wooden piles?
8 Why do pipes carrying water to houses have to be heated?

Look at Figure 9.9.
9 What is a white-out?

Ⓕ Questions

▬ CASE STUDY OF NORTH-WEST TERRITORIES, CANADA

Look at Figure 9.12.
Ⓕ1 In how many months on Baffin Island is the temperature above freezing point?

Look at Figure 9.13.
Ⓕ2 For how many months of the year are there
  (a) 24 hours of daylight each day and
  (b) 0 hours of daylight each day?

Figure 9.10 A caribou (a 'walking department store')

Look at Figure 9.15.

F3 Why has the caribou been so useful to the native Inuit and Indian people in this area?

Look at Figure 9.16.

F4 Why is mining here so expensive?

F5 What are the problems in drilling for oil in the sea?

Look at Figure 9.17.

F6 Which is the easier way of travelling in winter: by road or by air? Give reasons for your answer.

Look at Figure 9.18.

F7 What makes some houses in the tundra start to sink?

F8 Why can sewage and water pipes not be buried underground?

F9 Would you enjoy living in this climate? Give reasons for your answer.

G Questions

CASE STUDY OF NORTH-WEST TERRITORIES, CANADA

Look at Figure 9.12.

G1 Describe the changes in temperature throughout the year on Baffin Island.

Look at Figure 9.13.

G2 Describe the changes in the amount of daylight throughout the year on Baffin Island.

Look at Figure 9.15.

G3 Describe the importance of animals to the Inuit and Indian people.

Look at Figure 9.17.

G4 Coppermine is a small settlement on the north coast (see Figure 9.14). Do you think its supplies are brought in by ship or by lorry? Give reasons for your answer.

Look at Figure 9.18.

G5 Describe the problems faced by house builders because of the climate.

Look at Figures 9.17 and 9.20.

G6 What are the advantages and disadvantages of northern Canada for tourism?

CASE STUDY OF NORTH-WEST TERRITORIES, CANADA

Figure 9.11

Introduction

North-west Territories is a huge area of Northern Canada that includes thousands of islands in the Arctic Ocean. The people who first lived here were the Indians and Inuit (once called Eskimo) and they make up one-third of all the people who live here now. In 1999 a large part of this region will become a separate Inuit territory called **Nunavut**.

The **tree-line** runs across North-west Territories. South of it are vast areas of coniferous forests. North of it is treeless tundra where the climate presents formidable problems to the people.

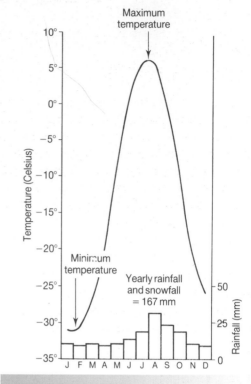

Figure 9.12 The climate of Baffin Island

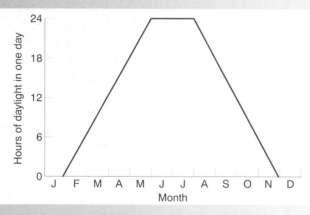

Figure 9.13 The amount of daylight on Baffin Island

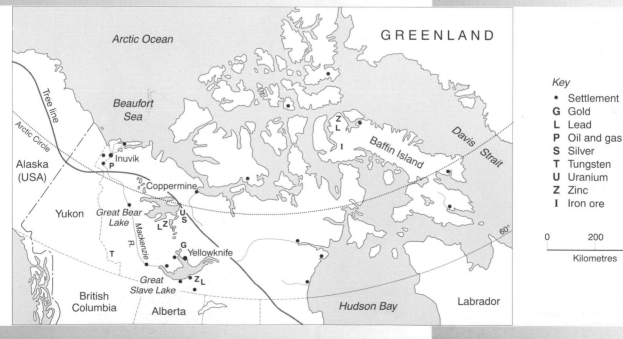

Figure 9.14 North-West Territories, Canada

★ RESOURCES ★

Figure 9.15

Traditional Way of Life

The first or indigenous people of this region were the Inuit in the north and the Indians further south. They lived by hunting and fishing. Even in such a harsh climate there were many animals to hunt (for example Arctic foxes, beavers, seals, polar bears and muskrats) but by far the most important was the **caribou**.

The caribou is a close relative of the reindeer and is known as a 'walking department store'. It not only provides food (from its meat) and clothes (from its skin), but also fuel (from its fat), tools and weapons (from its bones), and its skin is used to make kayaks and summer tents. The caribou migrate during the year to find fresh grazing and so too do the Inuit and Indians. Transport is by sledge, pulled by dog teams. This way of life began to change 200 years ago when outsiders first came in search of furs and, later, in search of minerals.

Figure 9.16

Minerals

Figure 9.14 shows that North-west Territories has a wealth of minerals, especially zinc and lead. Mining operations, however, are very expensive. Every nut, bolt, plank of wood and bag of cement has to be brought over 1000 km. Miners have to be paid high wages and they usually work seven days on and seven days off, so they can go home during their time off.

Mining companies are now exploring for oil in the waters north of Canada but drilling is complicated when the sea is frozen for much of the year. It is even more dangerous in summer when the sea ice begins to melt and oil rigs can be crushed between floating icebergs.

Figure 9.17

Transport

There are few roads and even fewer railways in this region and the permafrost is to blame. In summer the top layer of soil thaws out, causing roads to sink and railway lines to buckle. Because of this, roads and railways have to be built on gravel and covered by a sheet of insulation to prevent the soil thawing.

The cheapest form of transport is by water, but in winter the rivers and the sea water near the coast are frozen. Water transport can therefore only be used in the three summer months. In winter, cars and lorries can drive on 'ice roads' over frozen water. These are open for about four months while the ice is over 1 m thick.

Air transport is the quickest form of transport but is difficult in winter because of freezing fog, white-outs and high winds. Even in summer, fog is a hazard.

Figure 9.18

Settlement

The North-west Territories are 40 times larger than Scotland yet fewer people live here than in East Kilbride. Living conditions are made particularly difficult by the permafrost. If houses are not specially built, their heat will melt the frozen ground and cause the house to sink. Most buildings are therefore built on wooden or concrete piles. These piles are frozen into holes drilled into the permafrost.

   Again, because of the permafrost, gas, water and sewage pipes cannot be buried, as is done in our climate. When the top layer of soil thaws in summer, the pipes would sink and crack. So **utilidors** are built. These are long, heated boxes that carry the pipes above ground.

Figure 9.19

Rivers and Lakes

There are thousands of lakes in this region, including two of the biggest in North America: Great Bear Lake and Great Slave Lake. The most important river is the Mackenzie, which forms a delta when it enters the Beaufort Sea. Some of the rivers are used to create hydroelectricity, which accounts for 45 per cent of all electricity used in the North-west Territories. It has even been proposed that some of the rivers should be diverted southwards to those areas of North America where water is in very short supply.

Figure 9.20

Tourism

Tens of thousands of tourists visit this area every year, attracted by the unspoiled landscapes and the opportunities for fishing and hunting. There are four National Parks here, where the precious wilderness areas are protected from any mineral or energy projects.

Figure 9.21 Buildings subsiding due to permafrost

Figure 9.22 Heated utilidor carrying power and water

Extension Text

91 CLIMATE, VEGETATION AND SOIL

Vegetation needs heat and moisture to grow, therefore the type of vegetation that grows in any area depends very much on its climate. As a result, places with a similar climate usually have the same type of vegetation. For example, rainforest grows in an equatorial climate and broad-leaved woodland grows in a British climate.

The vegetation, in turn, strongly influences the soil underneath. Decaying roots, leaves and branches from the vegetation gradually decompose into a black substance called **humus**. This makes soil more fertile. Climates that support a lot of vegetation, especially grasslands, have soil improved by humus.

The climate also affects the soil. In Unit 5 we found out how wind and rain can erode soil. Rain also has a direct effect as it seeps through the soil and takes some of the minerals away in solution. This is called **leaching**. These minerals are important plant foods, so leaching reduces the fertility of a soil. As a result, rainy climates have soils that have been made poorer by leaching.

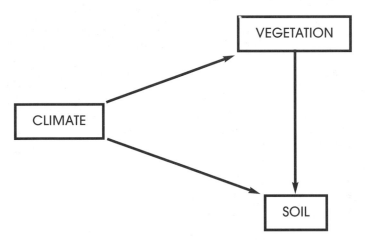

Equatorial soils
- a lot of humus from dense vegetation
- vegetation decomposes very quickly
- there is a lot of leaching by heavy rain every day

Hot desert soils
- very little humus because little vegetation
- vegetation does not decompose quickly without water
- soils are not leached

Mediterranean soils
- some humus from woodland vegetation
- vegetation decomposes quickly in the warm climate
- some leaching during winter rains

Tundra soils
- very little humus because very little vegetation
- vegetation decomposes very slowly
- no leaching because little precipitation
- a lot of waterlogging because of impermeable permafrost below

E Questions

Read the Extension Text.

E1 Why do places with a similar climate usually have similar vegetation?

E2 What is humus?

E3 In what way does the vegetation affect the soil underneath?

E4 What is leaching?

E5 In what ways does the climate affect the soil?

E6 Why are most equatorial soils quite poor in quality?

C Questions

CASE STUDY OF NORTH-WEST TERRITORIES, CANADA

Look at Figures 9.12 and 9.13.

C1 Contrast the temperature, rainfall and amount of daylight between winter and summer on Baffin Island.

Look at Figure 9.14.

C2 Describe the distribution of settlement in North-west Territories.

Look at Figures 9.17 and 9.18.

C3 Describe the problems that result from the permafrost in this area.

Look at Figure 9.16.

C4 Which is the bigger problem for mining companies in North-west Territories: recruiting workers or transporting materials to and from the mine? Give reasons for your answer.

Look at Figures 9.19 and 9.20.

C5 Apart from minerals, describe the other natural resources of the tundra region of the North-west Territories.

UNIT ⑩

Skills in Physical Landscape Studies

10A INTRODUCTION

High mountains and deep valleys, steep cliffs and flat plains, fast-flowing rivers and slow-moving sheets of ice are all part of our natural scenery or physical landscape. It is our job in geography to know how these landscapes have formed and the different ways in which they affect people

For the Standard Grade examination you need to know:
1 the features made by moving ice,
2 the features made by rivers,
3 the processes by which ice erodes and deposits,
4 the processes by which rivers erode and deposit, and
5 how the physical landscape affects the ways in which the land is used.

You also need to develop the following enquiry skills:
1 how to gather information on the physical landscape by field sketching and measuring rivers,
2 how to process this information by annotating field sketches and drawing pie graphs, and
3 how to analyse information about the physical landscape.

The rest of this unit deals with ways of gathering and processing information.

10B GATHERING INFORMATION

Many techniques can be used to gather information on the physical landscape. Some of the techniques that can be used to investigate the topics studied for Standard Grade are shown below.

Topic studied	Gathering technique
River characteristics	Measuring the river; extracting information from maps
Landforms (river or glacial)	Field sketching; extracting information from maps
Land use conflicts	Interviewing people involved; using a questionnaire to find out people's opinions

Some of these techniques are now described in detail.

10C MEASURING RIVER SPEED

River speed can be measured in the following way:

- take a recording sheet, float, watch and two markers to the river
- choose a site on the river that is safe and is typical of that stretch of the river
- decide where you wish to measure the speed: in the middle or at the side of the river (the river will be faster in the middle)
- set up two markers (for example two long sticks) along the river bank and measure the distance between them
- place a float (for example an orange, a table tennis ball or a cork) in the river
- find out how long the float takes to travel between the two markers (if the float becomes trapped, start again)
- repeat this five times
- work out an average time
- work out the average speed using the formula:

$$\text{average speed (metres per second)} = \frac{\text{distance travelled (metres)}}{\text{average time (seconds)}}$$

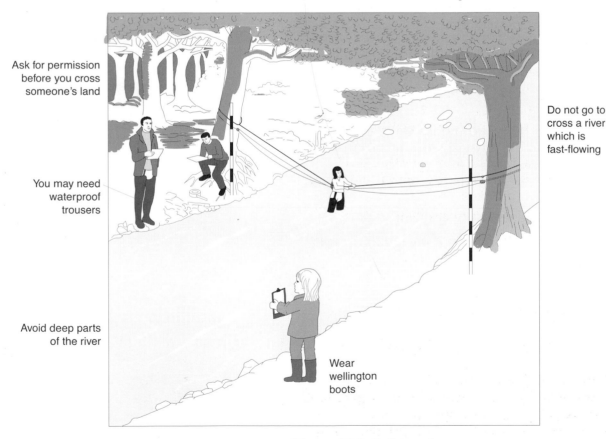

Ask for permission before you cross someone's land

Do not go to cross a river which is fast-flowing

You may need waterproof trousers

Avoid deep parts of the river

Wear wellington boots

Figure 10.1 Safety rules

10D MEASURING RIVER WIDTH

River width can be measured in the following way:

- take a recording sheet and measuring tape to a suitable site on the river

- decide whether you are going to measure from the top of the river bank or from the edge of the river, remembering that in summer the river may be much narrower than its channel
- measure the shortest distance across the river in metres
- take one step downstream and measure again
- repeat this until you have five widths
- work out the average width.

10E MEASURING RIVER DEPTH

River depth can be measured in the following way:
- take a recording sheet and measuring pole to a suitable site on the river
- decide where you are going to measure the depth: in the middle, at the sides or at several places across the river (for example 1 m apart)
- measure the depth using a measuring pole
- take one step downstream and measure again
- repeat this until you have five depths
- work out the average depth.

10F MEASURING RIVER BEDLOAD

Bedload is the pebbles and boulders that roll along a river bed. It can be measured in the following way:
- take a recording sheet and measuring tape to a suitable site on the river
- take a sample of stones by going into the middle of the river, reaching down and taking the first stone you touch
- repeat this until you have ten stones
- work out the size of each stone by measuring its long axis (its longest length)
- estimate the roundness of each stone on a scale of 1 to 10 (1 = very sharp and angular; 10 = completely round with no sharp edges)
- work out the average size and average roundness of your sample of stones.

10G FIELD SKETCHING

Field sketches can be made in the following way:
- take blank paper, a clipboard, a pencil and rubber to the site to be drawn
- choose a site where you can see clearly all the features you wish to sketch
- on your paper draw a frame for the sketch
- draw a line to show the skyline and another for the foreground
- draw the outline shape of the main landforms
- use thinner, shorter lines to show slopes and smaller features
- keep the sketch simple, only include the features you are studying
- estimate the heights of important features and the distance to them
- around the frame, label the names of the features
- give the sketch a title, a grid reference and an indication of which direction you were facing.

10H PROCESSING TECHNIQUES

A variety of processing techniques can be used to show all the information you have collected about the physical landscape. Two of these techniques are now studied in detail.

10J DRAWING A PIE GRAPH

A pie graph is used to show how one amount is shared out. Pie graphs are circles divided into slices or segments. Each segment shows an amount: the bigger the segment, the bigger the amount. Each segment is worked out in degrees and the segments together add up to 360°. A pie graph can be drawn in the following way:

- work out or find out the number of degrees in each segment, for example column 3 in Figure 10.2
- work out the size of each segment using a protractor or, if there is one, the scale around the edge of the circle (see Figure 10.4)
- draw the first segment in pencil, starting from the top of the circle and going clockwise; it is usually best to start with the smallest segment
- draw in the second smallest segment, next to the first
- continue drawing in segments of increasing size until you have finished
- shade in and label each segment
- give the pie graph a title.

Figure 10.2

Bedload of River Tweed near Kelso (GR 708374)

Size of stones (cm)	Number of stones	Degrees on pie graph
0–5	8	144
5–10	4	72
10–15	2	36
15–20	3	54
20–25	2	36
25 or more	1	18

Figure 10.3

Calculating the degrees in each segment of a pie graph:
- add up the total number of what you are measuring in all the segments (for example in Table 10.1 there are 20 stones in total)
- for each segment, divide its number by the total and then multiply by 360: this gives you the number of degrees for that segment (for example in Table 10.1) the segment for stones 0–5 cm in size =

$$\frac{8}{20} \times 360 = 144°$$

- repeat this calculation for all the segments
- check that the total number of degrees adds up to 360.

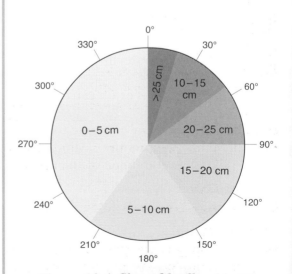

Figure 10.4 Size of bedload in River Tweed near Kelso (GR 708374)

10K ANNOTATING A FIELD SKETCH

The field sketch drawn at the site should be annotated as follows:
- draw a neat copy of your field sketch when you are back indoors
- label only the features that are important to your study, for example in Figure 10.5, if you are studying weather stations, label only the features which affect the weather station
- write the name clearly beside each feature, using an arrow if necessary
- use arrows sparingly and make sure they do not cross
- do not write too many names, otherwise your sketch will become too cluttered.

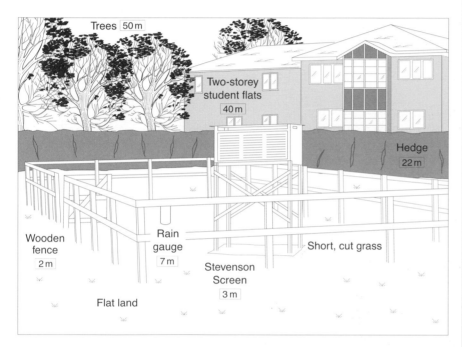

Figure 10.5 Annotated field sketch of Stirling University's weather station

ⒻQuestions

Look at 10B.

Ⓕ1 What technique would you use to gather details about
 (a) a local waterfall and
 (b) a conflict over a new quarry being started?

Look at 10C.

Ⓕ2 (a) What equipment do you need to measure river speed?
 (b) What is each piece of equipment used for?

Look at 10D.

Ⓕ3 Describe how you would measure the width of a river.

Look at 10J.

Ⓕ4 (a) Copy the pie graph in Figure 10.6.
 (b) Complete the pie graph using information in Figure 10.7 overleaf.

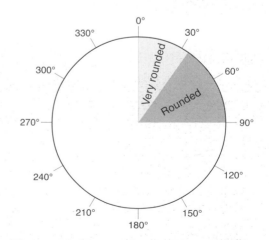

Figure 10.6 Roundness of bedload in a river

Figure 10.7

Roundness of bedload	Number of stones	Degrees on pie graph
Very rounded	2	36
Rounded	3	54
Quite rounded	3	54
Angular	5	90
Very angular	7	126

Look at the tables below.

F5 Which table, Figure 10.8 or 10.9, would be better shown by a pie graph?

Figure 10.8

Width of River Teviot

Site on River Teviot	Average width of River Teviot (m)
Site A (upper course)	1.5
Site B (middle course)	4.7
Site C (lower course)	11.3

Figure 10.9

Bedload size in River Teviot

Bedload size at site C	Number of stones
Cobbles	5
Boulders	1
Stones	14

Figure 10.10

Depth across River Teviot

Depth of river at site C (cm)	Distance from left-hand bank (m)
25	2
110	4
185	6
175	8
52	10

G Questions

Look at 10B.

G1 Name one technique you would use to study changes along the course of a river. Give a reason for your answer.

Look at 10C.

G2 Describe some problems that may occur when trying to measure river speed.

Look at 10D.

G3 Why is it necessary to measure river width several times and take an average?

Look at 10E.

G4 Describe how you would measure the depth of a river.

Look at 10J.

G5 Draw a pie graph to show the information in the table below.

Bedload size in river's upper course (cm)	Number of stones	Degrees on pie graph
0–5	6	108
5–10	3	54
10–15	1	18
15–20	1	18
20–25	4	72
25 or more	5	90

Look at Figures 10.8 and 10.9 under the F Questions

G6 Which table, Figure 10.8 or 10.9, would be better shown by a pie graph? Give a reason for your answer.

C Questions

Look at 10B.

C1 What techniques would you use to investigate the influence of the physical landscape on land uses in a small area? Explain your answer.

Look at 10C.

C2 When measuring river speed, explain why it is necessary to take several measurements at each site.

Look at 10F.

C3 Describe how you would measure the bedload of a river.

Look at 10J and Figure 10.11.

C4 Draw a pie graph of the information shown in the table opposite.

Look at Figures 10.8, 10.9 and 10.10 under the F Questions.

C5 Which table, Figure 10.8, 10.9 or 10.10, would be best shown by a pie graph? Justify your answer.

Figure 10.11

Local opinion about new by-pass	Number of people
Very much in favour	4
In favour	6
Against	8
Very much against	10
Don't know	2

UNIT ⑪

Rivers and their Valleys

Core Text

11A RIVERS IN THE LANDSCAPE

Where a river starts is called its **source**. This is usually in an upland area. All the rain that falls in the surrounding area flows into the river. This area is called the river's **catchment area**. The river flows downstream and is joined by **tributaries** – streams that flow into the river. Finally the river ends, either in another river or in the sea. Where the river ends is called its **mouth**.

As it flows downstream, a river helps to shape the physical landscape. It removes soil and rocks (**erosion**), carries them to a different area (**transportation**) and then drops them (**deposition**).

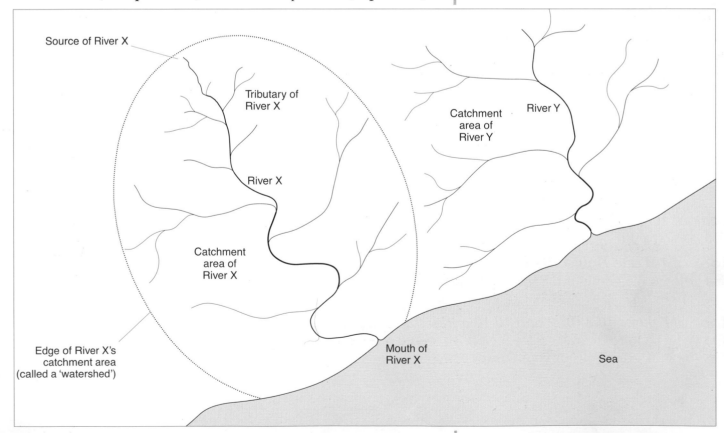

Figure 11.1 A river's catchment area

11B HOW RIVERS SHAPE THE LANDSCAPE

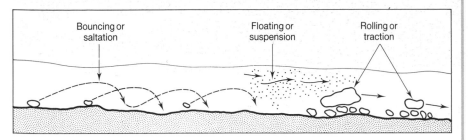

Figure 11.2 How a river carries its load

The amount of water in a river is called its **volume**. A river's volume and its speed give it **energy** to carry and erode soil and rocks. The soil and rocks that a river carries are called its **load**.

If a river has a lot of energy, it can carry small particles and large rocks. Small particles float in the water. Large pebbles and boulders bounce or roll along the bed (see Figure 11.2). As they bounce and roll, they break up the rock underneath. In time, pieces of the rock break off and are carried away by the river. In this way the river erodes a valley.

The river's load is also eroded. As stones hit the river bed or rub against each other, they are worn down and become smaller and more rounded.

If a river has very little energy, it cannot carry much load so it deposits some, always dropping the biggest rocks first.

11C THE COURSE OF A RIVER

Figure 11.3 shows how a river changes as it flows downstream. Because it changes so much, it is helpful to divide its course into three stages: the **upper course**, the **middle course** and the **lower course**.

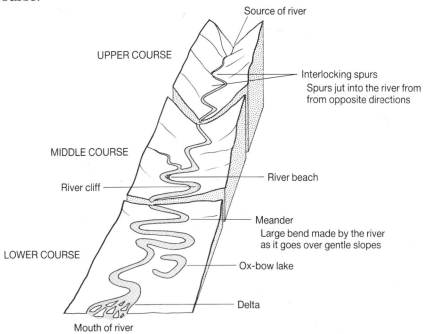

Figure 11.3 Changes along a river

11D RIVERS ON MAPS

When describing a river from an OS map you should mention the following:
- its direction
- its width (from the thickness of the blue line)
- its slope (from the number of contours it crosses)
- its straightness
- its landforms: waterfalls, river beaches, meanders, etc.
- its volume (from the number of tributaries joining it).

When describing a river valley you should mention:
- its direction
- its straightness
- its width (the distance between the first contours either side of the river)
- its slope (from the closeness of the contours)
- its landforms: ox-bow lakes, flood plain, etc.

11E LANDFORMS IN A RIVER'S UPPER COURSE

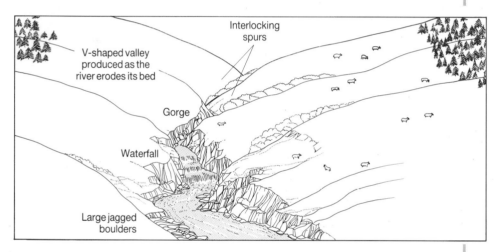

Figure 11.4 A river's upper course

In its upper course a river is narrow, shallow and flows through a V-shaped valley. It flows down steep slopes and has little load to carry so most of its energy is used to erode. The main landforms in its upper course are therefore produced by erosion.

11F WATERFALLS

Waterfalls are formed in the following way:
- the river flows over areas of hard and soft rock, eroding soft rock more quickly than hard rock
- hard rock sticks out, causing a **waterfall**
- the soft rock at the bottom of the waterfall is eroded to form a **plunge pool**
- rock above plunge pool collapses and the waterfall moves back.

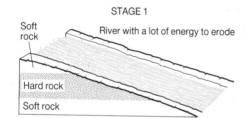

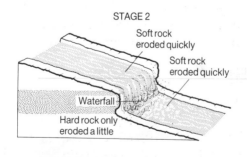

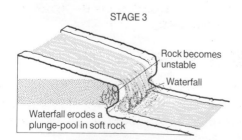

Figure 11.5 Stages in the formation of a waterfall

11G THE UPPER COURSE AND PEOPLE

The features of a river's upper course affect the people living there:

- fast-flowing water can be used for generating hydroelectric power
- steep valley sides are difficult to farm and build on
- the water is usually too shallow for ships to use
- a narrow river is easy to dam to make a reservoir
- waterfalls and steep slopes attract sightseers
- fast-flowing 'white water' is suitable for canoeing and other water sports
- waterfalls prevent ships using the river.

11H LANDFORMS IN A RIVER'S MIDDLE COURSE

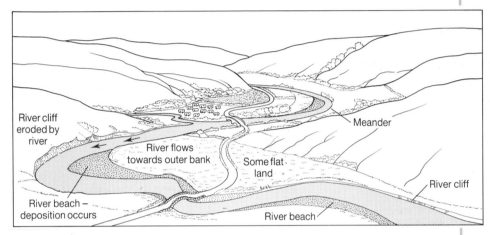

Figure 11.6 A river's middle course

In its middle course the river is flowing over a more gentle slope. It is wider and deeper and it meanders over a narrow valley floor. It carries more load, which is made up of smaller particles.

Because the river has more load to carry, it has less energy left to erode its bed. In the middle course, therefore, some landforms are produced by deposition and some by erosion.

11J RIVER CLIFFS

River cliffs are formed in the following way:

- the river flows towards the outer bend of a meander
- the river has a lot of energy at the outer bend and erodes the bottom of the river bank
- the river undercuts the bank, making a steeper slope called a **river cliff**.

11K RIVER BEACHES

River beaches are formed in the following way:

- the river flows slowly on the inner bend of a meander
- the river has less energy on the inner bend than on the outer bend
- the river has to deposit some of its load on the inner bend and makes a **river beach**.

11L THE MIDDLE COURSE AND PEOPLE

The features of a river's middle course affect the people living on there:

- there is a small area of flat land suitable for building
- the flat valley floor is a useful route for roads and railways
- the flat land is suitable for caravan sites, picnic sites, etc.
- farmers can grow crops on the flat land
- the river is usually too shallow for ships to use.

11M LANDFORMS IN A RIVER'S LOWER COURSE

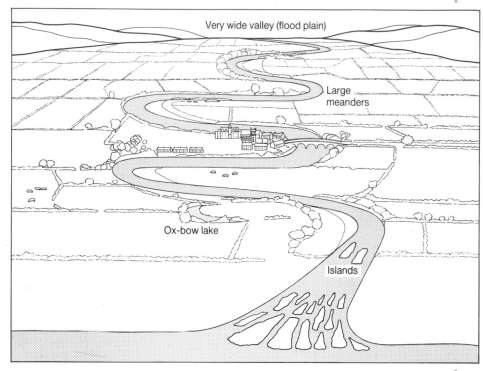

Very wide valley (flood plain)

Large meanders

Ox-bow lake

Islands

Figure 11.7 A river's lower course

In its lower course the river is much wider, deeper and has more meanders. It has a wide flat valley floor called a **flood plain**. The river also carries a large load and uses all of its energy to carry this load. In some places it does not have enough energy and so it deposits part of its load. As a result, most of the landforms in the lower course are produced by deposition.

11N OX-BOW LAKES

Ox-bow lakes are formed in the following way:

- the river meanders in its valley
- when the river floods it has enough energy to erode a new channel across the meander
- the old meander is separated from the river and is left as an **ox-bow lake**
- in time the lake will evaporate or silt up.

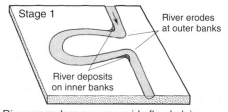

Stage 1

River erodes at outer banks

River deposits on inner banks

River meanders across a wide flood-plain

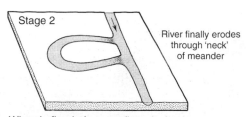

Stage 2

River finally erodes through 'neck' of meander

When in flood, river overflows its banks and erodes a new channel

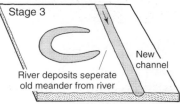

Stage 3

New channel

River deposits seperate old meander from river

Old meander is left as an ox-bow lake

Figure 11.8 Formation of an ox-bow lake

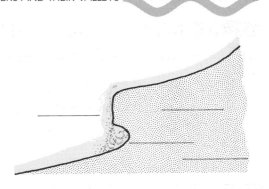

Figure 11.9

11P THE LOWER COURSE AND PEOPLE

The features of a river's lower course affect the people living there:
* the flat valley floor provides suitable land for farming and building on
* flat land is easily flooded; **embankments** are sometimes built to prevent this
* deep water is suitable for ships and the river can be **dredged** to make it even deeper
* meanders are difficult for ships to navigate but they can be straightened.

Core Questions

Look at 11A.

1 What name is given to the place where
 (a) a river starts and
 (b) a river ends?

2 What is a river's catchment area?

Look at 11B.

3 Explain how a river erodes a valley.

Look at Figure 11.3.

4 Describe four ways in which a river changes as it goes downstream.

Look at 11F.

5 Copy Figure 11.9.
 Write in the missing words, choosing from hard rock, soft rock, plunge pool, waterfall.

Look at 11E, 11F, 11J, 11K and 11N.

6 Explain how an ox-bow lake forms.

7 Copy and complete Figure 11.10 by writing the following landforms into the correct column of the table: V-shaped valley, waterfall, river beach, river cliff, ox-bow lake.

Figure 11.10	
River landforms produced by erosion	River landforms produced by deposition

Look at 11P.

8 Why are embankments built beside a river?

9 Why is a river dredged?

ⓕ Questions

■ CASE STUDY OF THE RIVER TEES

Look at Figure 11.12.

F1 Describe the main landforms along the River Tees.

Look at Figure 11.13.

F2 Describe the main settlements that the River Tees passes through.

Look at Figures 11.14 and 11.18.

F3 Do you think many tourists visit the upper course of the River Tees? Give reasons for your answer.

Look at Figures 11.15 and 11.18.

F4 How do you think High Force waterfall formed?

F5 Suggest how the river cliff in Figure 11.11 was formed.

Figure 11.11 River cliff on the River Tees

Look at Figure 11.16.

F6 Is the River Tees valley good for farming in its middle course? Give reasons for your answer.

Look at Figure 11.20.

F7 Describe how the river bend at Thornaby in Figure 11.20 might become a lake.

Look at Figure 11.17.

F8 Describe the types of industry found in the lower course of the River Tees.

F9 Draw a field sketch of the area shown in Figure 11.19. Label the sketch to show the main river features.

ⓖ Questions

■ CASE STUDY OF THE RIVER TEES

Look at Figure 11.12.

G1 Describe the main landforms in the upper, middle and lower courses of the River Tees.

Look at Figure 11.13.

G2 Describe the distribution of settlements along the course of the River Tees.

Look at Figures 11.15 and 11.18.

G3 With the aid of a diagram, describe how High Force waterfall might have formed.

Look at Figures 11.14 and 11.16.

G4 Compare the farming in the upper and middle courses of the River Tees.

G5 Describe what might happen in time to the shape of the River Tees, shown in Figure 11.20.

Look at Figure 11.17.

G6 Describe the advantages and disadvantages of the lower course of the River Tees as a port.

G7 Draw a field sketch of the area shown in Figure 11.19. Label the sketch to show the main river features.

CASE STUDY OF THE RIVER TEES

Figure 11.12

Introduction

The River Tees rises on the side of Cross Fell, the second highest mountain in England. From its source it flows over waterfalls and rapids and has carved out a V-shaped valley. From the town of Barnard Castle its valley becomes wider, the slope becomes gentler and the river has meanders and river cliffs. East of Darlington, the river meanders more and more and even has ox-bow lakes. Finally, at its mouth it widens out to be the Tees Estuary and enters the deep and stormy North Sea.

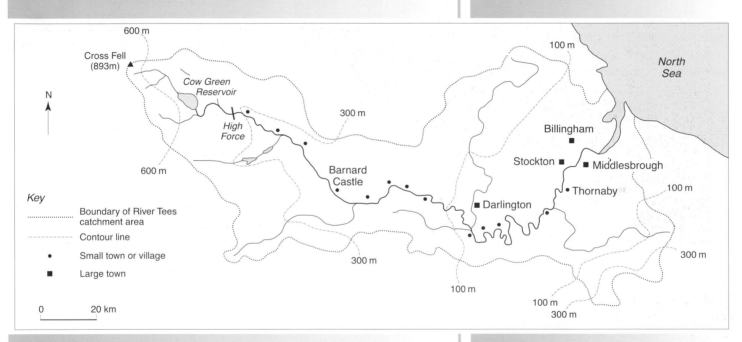

Figure 11.13 Catchment area of the River Tees

Figure 11.14

The Upper Course

The steep slopes of the River Tees valley in its upper course are used mainly by farmers for rearing sheep and beef cattle. There is a little flat land, which is used for buildings and for growing hay and silage as winter fodder for the animals. The steepest slopes cannot be farmed and are given over to woodland. Part of the valley can be reached by a secondary road, but the first 10 km, with its waterfalls and rapids, can only be reached on foot. In 1971, over 3 square km of this remote valley was flooded to create Cow Green reservoir.

Figure 11.15

High Force Waterfall

At High Force, the River Tees drops vertically for 27 m, making it the highest waterfall in England. The rock at the top of the waterfall is very hard whinstone. At the bottom is much softer limestone, which has been eroded to form a cave or plunge pool (see Figure 11.18).

Figure 11.16

The Middle Course

By the time it reaches Barnard Castle, the River Tees has dropped over 600 m in height and therefore the valley is much warmer, drier and sunnier. There is also more flat land and the valley sides are more gently sloping. Farmers need to add lime to the soil because it is still quite acid and they need to drain the valley floor because it can be quite marshy. It is an area of mixed farming, with oats, barley and potatoes grown on the flatter land and sheep and cattle grazing the valley sides. In the past the river was used for water power and it is still used by local towns and villages as a water supply and for dumping sewage.

Figure 11.17

The Lower Course

The river here meanders through a wide flat valley. It is prone to flooding and embankments have been built at various places along the river to reduce this risk. Once the land has been drained it is very fertile and a range of crops are grown, for example wheat, barley, potatoes, beans, peas, linseed and oilseed rape. Sheep are also brought down from the hills to be fattened here on the lusher grass.

There are many settlements in this part of the river's course. In early years, people built settlements inside meanders, such as at Yarm, as they were easy to defend. At its mouth, the river is sheltered and tidal, and so ports, such as Middlesbrough and Stockton, grew up here in the nineteenth century. The river was too meandering and too shallow for large ships to use, but it has been dredged and straightened over the years. It attracted shipyards and industries such as steelworks, chemical works and power stations, which needed large amounts of water. Many of these industries have now closed down and the riverside area has undergone much redevelopment.

Figure 11.18 High Force waterfall

Figure 11.19 The River Tees in its middle course

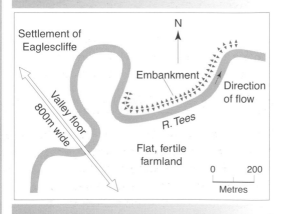

Figure 11.20 River Tees west of Thornaby

Extension Text

11Q LEVÉES

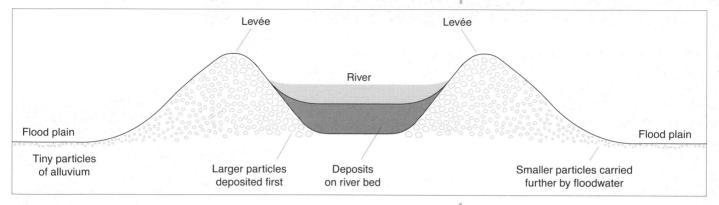

Figure 11.21 A levée

Levées are formed in the following way:
- in its lower course the river may flood over its flood plain
- when the flood recedes, silt and mud are left behind, making a fertile soil called **alluvium**
- most alluvium is dropped when the floor water slows down as soon as it overflows the river banks
- on the river banks, natural embankments of alluvium build up; these are called **levées**
- the flood water deposits its largest particles first, on the levée and carries the finer particles further onto the flood plain
- the river continues to deposit material on its bed and gradually rises above its flood plain
- levées protect the flood plain from flooding.

11R DELTAS

Deltas are formed in the following way:
- at the end of its course the river flows into a shallow sea with weak tides
- the river's speed is checked and it deposits its load, largest particles first
- the alluvium builds up above sea level to form a **delta**
- the deposited material forces the river to **braid**, that is divide into channels called **distributaries**.

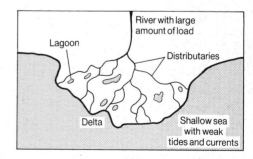

Figure 11.22 A delta

11S LATERAL AND VERTICAL EROSION

During its course, the river erodes both vertically and laterally. In its upper course the river carries large rocks, which break up the rock below by bouncing (**saltation**) and rolling (**traction**) along the river bed. This is **vertical erosion**. The river is eroding downwards and making a V-shaped valley. In its lower course the river carries much smaller particles and it does far less vertical erosion. Instead, because it is meandering, when it does erode it does so at its sides. This is called **lateral erosion**. By this means it forms river cliffs and ox-bow lakes.

E Questions

Read the Extension Text.

E1 What is alluvium?

E2 Explain how levées form.

E3 Describe the conditions necessary for deltas to form.

E4 What is braiding?

E5 Explain why most rivers do not have deltas.

E6 What is the difference between vertical erosion and lateral erosion?

C Questions

■ CASE STUDY OF THE RIVER TEES

Look at Figures 11.12 and 11.13.

C1 Describe the location and height of the upper, middle and lower courses of the River Tees.

Look at Figures 11.15 and 11.18.

C2 Suggest how High Force waterfall has retreated over time, leaving a gorge in its place.

Look at Figures 11.16 and 11.17.

C3 Compare the suitability of the Tees valley for farming in its middle and lower courses.

C4 Explain, with the aid of diagrams, how the course of the River Tees near Thornaby (shown in Figure 11.20) is likely to change in the future.

Look at Figure 11.17.

C5 Describe the ways in which the lower course of the River Tees and its valley has been useful to people.

Look at Figures 11.12 and 11.17.

C6 Why do you think the River Tees has no delta at its mouth?

C7 Draw a field sketch of the area shown in Figure 11.19. Annotate the sketch to show the main river landforms.

Landforms made by Ice Erosion

Core Text

12A THE ICE ACE

About two million years ago our climate began to get colder. Rain turned to snow, which built up on hills and turned to ice. The Ice Age had begun.

As more snow fell, the ice beneath was squeezed out and began to move slowly down the mountainside. This ice was called a **glacier**. When the ice reached the foot of the mountain, it joined with other glaciers to make a huge **ice sheet**. The ice sheet moved slowly southwards, joining with ice from Norway and Sweden. Very soon nearly all of Britain and northern Europe was buried under hundreds of metres of ice.

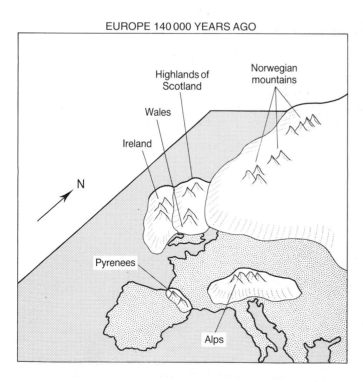

Figure 12.1 Europe during the Ice Age

12B HOW ICE SHAPED OUR LANDSCAPE

The glaciers and ice sheets were very powerful. The ice froze onto rocks and, as it moved, tore pieces away. This process eroded vast amounts of rock, which the ice dropped, sometimes hundreds of kilometres away. Figure 12.2 shows how the ice changed the shape of our upland areas. Some of these landforms are now described in more detail.

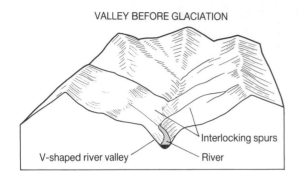

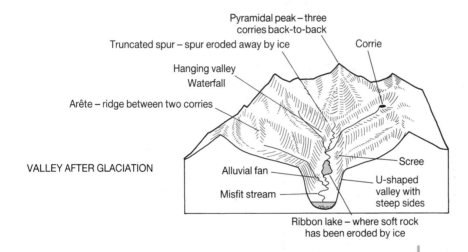

Figure 12.2 A valley before (above) and after (below) glaciation

12C CORRIES

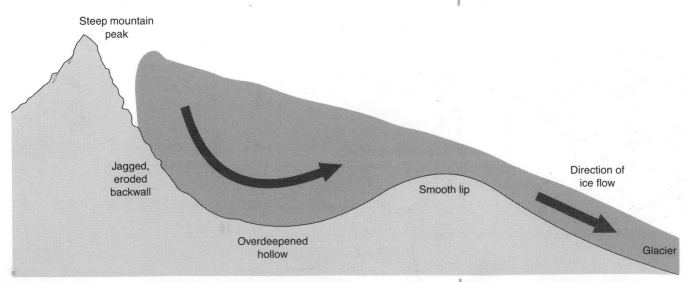

Figure 12.3 How a corrie forms

Corries are steep-sided hollows high up in the mountains. They are formed in the following way:

- snow and ice collect in hollows high up
- as the ice moves down the mountainside, it erodes the back and bottom of the hollow
- a deep bowl-shaped hollow begins to form
- **corrie lochs** often fill the hollows after the ice has melted.

Corries may be useful to different people:

- the steep slopes and cold snowy winters attract skiers
- the lochs can be tourist attractions
- the lochs can be used as reservoirs for hydroelectric power schemes.

12D U-SHAPED VALLEYS

U-shaped valleys are formed in the following way:

- a glacier flows down an old V-shaped valley
- as the glacier flows, it erodes the sides and bottom of the valley
- the valley becomes U-shaped, with very steep sides and a flat bottom.

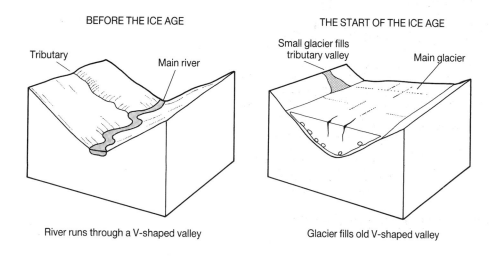

BEFORE THE ICE AGE

River runs through a V-shaped valley

THE START OF THE ICE AGE

Glacier fills old V-shaped valley

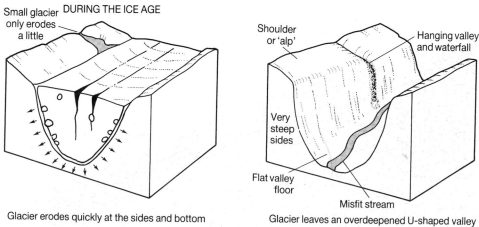

DURING THE ICE AGE

Glacier erodes quickly at the sides and bottom

AFTER THE ICE AGE

Glacier leaves an overdeepened U-shaped valley

Figure 12.4 How a U-shaped valley and hanging valley form

U-shaped valleys affect people in different ways:
- the very steep sides are difficult to farm and are often forested
- people can farm and build on the flat valley floor, but it is sometimes marshy
- the south-facing slopes are sunnier and warmer and used more than north-facing slopes
- the 'shoulder' of the valley may be used as summer pasture
- the dramatic scenery attracts many tourists throughout the year.

12E HANGING VALLEYS

Hanging valleys are formed in the following way:
- a thick glacier flows through the main valley, while a small glacier flows through a tributary valley (see Figure 12.4)
- the thick glacier erodes more deeply than the small glacier and therefore the tributary valley is left 'hanging' above the main valley
- after the Ice Age, a river may flow over the hanging valley as a waterfall.

Hanging valleys may be useful to different people:
- the waterfalls are tourist attractions
- the force of the water at waterfalls can be used to make hydro-electricity.

12F FIORDS

Fiords are formed in the following way:
- during the Ice Age, glaciers made U-shaped valleys
- some of the U-shaped valleys reached the sea
- after the Ice Age, all the melted ice returned to the sea and the sea-level rose
- the sea flooded the U-shaped valleys, making sea inlets
- these sea inlets in glaciated uplands are called fiords.

Fiords affect people in different ways:
- they are deep and sheltered and make excellent harbours
- few people live near them because the steep slopes make it difficult to build houses, roads and factories
- the fiords and mountains attract tourists
- the deep water can be used by large ships, such as oil tankers, and for making oil production platforms.

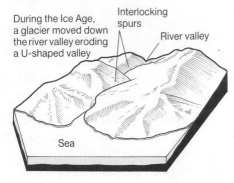

STAGE 1 BEFORE THE ICE AGE

During the Ice Age, a glacier moved down the river valley eroding a U-shaped valley

Interlocking spurs

River valley

Sea

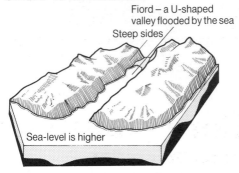

STAGE 2 AFTER THE ICE AGE

Fiord – a U-shaped valley flooded by the sea

Steep sides

Sea-level is higher

Figure 12.5 How a fiord forms

12G GLACIAL LANDFORMS ON MAPS

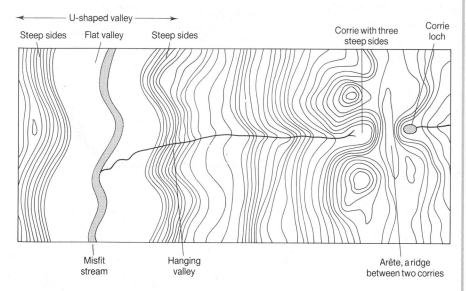

Figure 12.6

Core Questions

Look at 12B.

1 Name features A to F in Figure 12.7. Choose from corrie, U-shaped valley, truncated spur, arête, hanging valley, ribbon lake.

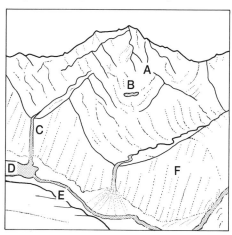

Figure 12.7 A glaciated upland

Look at 12C.

2 What is often found in the hollow of a corrie?

Look at 12D.

3 How do U-shaped valleys form?

Look at 12E.

4 Why does a glacier erode a main valley more than a tributary valley?

5 What does a hanging valley sometimes become after the ice has melted?

Look at 12F.

6 Why did the sea level rise at the end of the Ice Age?

7 Why do fiords make excellent harbours?

8 Draw a field sketch of the area shown in Figure 12.8. Label the sketch to show the main glacial landforms.

F Questions

CASE STUDY OF LITTLE LANGDALE VALLEY, LAKE DISTRICT

Look at Figures 12.10 and 12.11.

F1 Describe some of the main landforms made by ice in Little Langdale valley.

F2 Little Langdale valley has a U-shape. Describe how it formed.

Look at Figure 12.13.

F3 Describe how ice made the small lake in the valley called Little Langdale Tarn.

Look at Figures 12.11 and 12.14.

F4 Which is the better farmland in Little Langdale: the valley floor or the lower slopes? Give reasons for your answer.

Look at Figure 12.11.

F5 Why do you think there are so few buildings close to the river?

F6 Which lake would make a better reservoir for the local people: Blea Tarn or Little Langdale Tarn? Give reasons for your answer.

F7 Which is the better place for a youth hostel: A or B in Figure 12.11? Give reasons for your answer.

F8 Why do you think most people live on the south-facing side of Little Langdale Valley?

Figure 12.8 A glaciated valley in Switzerland

Ⓖ Questions

CASE STUDY OF GREAT LANGDALE VALLEY, LAKE DISTRICT

Look at Figures 12.11 and 12.16.

Ⓖ1 Describe the location of glacial landforms in Great Langdale valley.

Look at Figure 12.17.

Ⓖ2 Describe how Stickle Tarn was formed.

Look at Figure 12.19.

Ⓖ3 Describe how Dungeon Ghyll Force was formed.

Look at Figures 12.11, 12.18 and 12.20.

Ⓖ4 Compare the land uses on the valley sides of Great Langdale valley with those on the valley floor.

Ⓖ5 What are the advantages and disadvantages of this area for tourism?

Look at Figure 12.11.

Ⓖ6 Describe the distribution of settlement along Great Langdale valley.

Ⓖ7 Which is the best location for a camp site: C, D or E in Figure 12.11? Give reasons for your answer.

★ RESOURCES ★

CASE STUDY OF THE LANGDALE AND EASEDALE VALLEYS, LAKE DISTRICT

Figure 12.9

Introduction

The Lake District is the highest upland area in England. During the Ice Age an ice-cap formed here and glaciers pushed outwards in all directions. The glaciers followed old river valleys, eroding very powerfully to produce many glacial landforms. The last glaciers finally melted 8000 years ago and their meltwater filled the eroded hollows to make the ribbon lakes for which the Lake District is famous.

During the depths of the Ice Age, three glaciers flowed eastwards from the ice-cap and occupied the Great Langdale valley, the Little Langdale valley and the Easedale valley. These valleys are shown in Figure 12.11 and are now studied in more detail.

Figure 12.10

Little Langdale Valley

The glacier that flowed through Little Langdale valley was quite thick and wide. It was joined by other smaller glaciers, including one flowing out of the corrie where Blea Tarn now is. The glacier flowed through an old V-shaped river valley. The sides and bottom of this valley were eroded by the ice freezing onto the rock and then tearing away pieces of rock as it moved. The V-shaped valley gradually became a much deeper U-shape, with hanging valleys and truncated spurs at its sides. The glacier eventually joined another one flowing through Great Langdale valley.

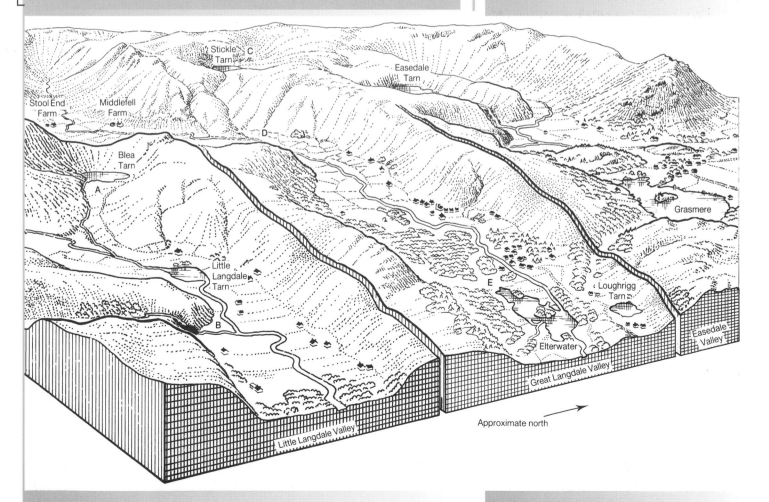

Figure 12.11 The Langdale and Easedale Valleys, Lake District

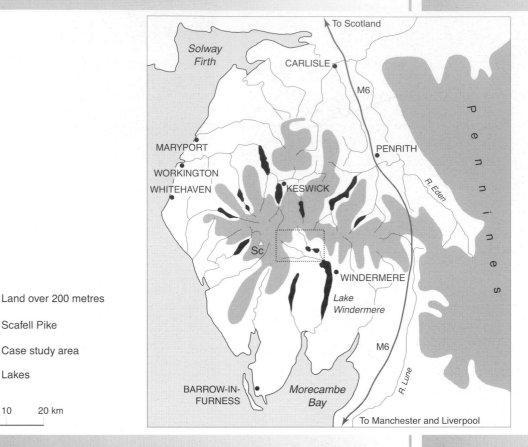

Key

Land over 200 metres

Sc △ Scafell Pike

Case study area

Lakes

0   10   20 km

Figure 12.12 The Lake District

Figure 12.13

Little Langdale Tarn

Where the glacier flowed over soft rock, it found it easier to tear away pieces of rock. A hollow was soon eroded in the soft rock. When the ice melted, this hollow was filled with water and became Little Langdale Tarn, shown in Figure 12.11.

Figure 12.14

Land Uses in Little Langdale

The valley floor is quite uneven and the soil is quite deep and fertile, but the river often floods and some of the land is marshy. It is mostly used for grazing sheep and cattle. The lower slopes are steeper and drier, but they are rocky and so machines cannot be used. Some woodland and pasture is found here. The upper slopes are very steep and are covered in heather and bracken. There are many bare rock cliffs.

Figure 12.15 Little Langdale

★ **RESOURCES** ★

Figure 12.16

Great Langdale Valley

At the same time as a glacier flowed through Little Langdale, another glacier was moving through Great Langdale. It was also joined by smaller glaciers flowing out of corries such as those at Stickle Tarn and Langdale Combe (see Figure 12.9). This glacier filled the valley up to 450 m, so high that some overflowed into Little Langdale. It gouged out a U-shaped valley, truncated the spurs of rock jutting into the valley and, where the rock was softer, it eroded hollows or **rock basins**. After the Ice Age most of Great Langdale was a huge lake, which gradually drained away. Elterwater, occupying a rock basin, also used to be much larger.

Figure 12.17

Stickle Tarn

At the start of the Ice Age, snow collected in a hollow high up on the side of Harrison Stickle. The snow filled the hollow, turned to ice and began to move out of the hollow as a glacier. As it did so, it tore away fragments of rock from the hollow onto which it had frozen and then scraped the rock with the fragments it was now carrying. In this way the sides and base of the hollow were eroded to form an armchair-shaped corrie. When the ice melted, this hollow filled with water to become Stickle Tarn.

Figure 12.18 Great Langdale valley

Figure 12.19

Dungeon Ghyll Force

The glacier coming out of this corrie was small and so did not have much power to erode a deep valley. The main glacier in Great Langdale was much thicker and eroded very deeply. By the end of the Ice Age, the valley leading out of Stickle Tarn corrie was 'hanging' well above Great Langdale valley and, once the ice melted, a waterfall began to flow over this hanging valley, called Dungeon Ghyll Force.

Figure 12.20

Land Uses in Great Langdale

The valley floor has fine soils laid down in an old lake, but the river is prone to flooding and the land is marshy and mainly used for grazing sheep and cattle and growing hay. The lower slopes are rockier and have a few farm buildings and hotels and the only road. The upper slopes are very steep and only useful as rough grazing for sheep.

Figure 12.21

Easedale Valley

The U-shaped valley of Easedale was also carved out by a glacier which flowed eastwards and was joined by other smaller glaciers, including one flowing out of the hollow now occupied by Easedale Tarn. The valley displays much evidence of powerful glacial erosion, with corries high up, hanging valleys and truncated spurs on the valley sides and roche moutonnées and rock basins on the valley floor. Scree material now covers some of the lower slopes and a waterfall cascades down the hanging valley into the misfit stream flowing through the valley floor.

Figure 12.22

Land Uses in Easedale Valley

Land uses here are very similar to those in Langdale, for similar reasons. The glacial features make it attractive to tourists but its limited access by road restricts the number of sightseers. Walkers, however, make use of the many public footpaths that traverse the area.

The environment makes farming difficult. The only crop grown is hay on the valley floor, but it is not enough for all the winter fodder needed for the sheep. The sheep winter on the valley floor but go up to the higher pastures in summer time. Farm buildings cling to the valley sides away from the valley floor, which is prone to flooding.

Extension Text

12H PROCESSES OF GLACIAL EROSION

Moving ice erodes in two ways:

plucking   ice freezes onto rocks and 'plucks' away loose fragments leaving a rough, jagged surface.

abrasion   fragments embedded in the bottom of the ice scrape and smooth the rock over which it is moving.

In glaciated areas, there is also **freeze–thaw action** in which meltwater enters cracks in the rock, freezes and expands. This forces the crack slightly wider. When this freeze–thaw action is repeated many times, pieces of rock are broken off. They often build up at the foot of slopes as **scree**.

12J A ROCHE MOUTONNÉE

This is a small rock outcrop in which one side is steeper than the other. It is formed in the following way:
- ice flows over an outcrop of hard rock
- ice abrades the upstream slope, smoothing it
- ice erodes the downstream slope much more by plucking, making it steeper
- a roche moutonnée is formed with one steep, jagged slope and one gentle, smooth slope.

12K A CRAG AND TAIL

A crag and tail formation occurs in the following way:
- ice approaches a very steep outcrop of hard rock (a **crag**)
- ice erodes softer rock upstream of the crag
- ice splits and moves around the crag, joining together behind it
- soft rock immediately behind the crag is eroded less and remains as higher land (**tail**)
- the best example in Scotland is Edinburgh's Castle Rock (crag) and the Royal Mile (tail)

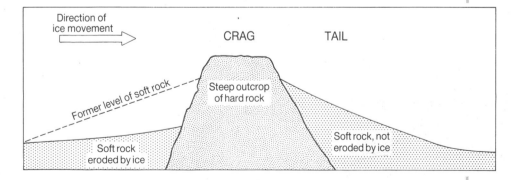

Figure 12.23 Formation of a crag and tail

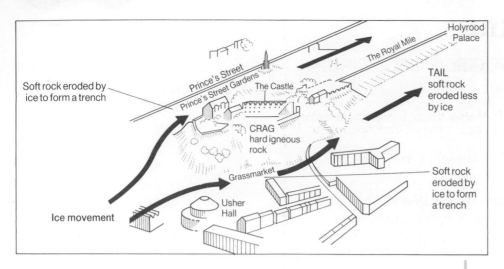

Figure 12.24 Edinburgh's crag and tail

E Questions

Read the Extension Text.

E1 Describe how freeze–thaw action breaks up rocks.

E2 What is a roche moutonnée?

E3 Explain how Edinburgh's Castle Rock and Royal Mile have been shaped by ice.

Look at 12C.

E4 Explain how (a) corries and (b) U-shaped valleys have been formed, using the terms plucking, abrasion, freeze–thaw action.

C Questions

CASE STUDY OF EASEDALE VALLEY, LAKE DISTRICT

Look at Figures 12.11 and 12.21.

C1 Describe the likely formation of Easedale Tarn. You may use a diagram to illustrate your answer.

C2 Suggest how ice may have formed the steep drop below Easedale Tarn now occupied by a waterfall.

C3 Within Easedale valley are small hills with one smooth gentle slope and one steep jagged slope. Describe how these hills might have formed.

C4 Suggest the likely origin of the scree material at the side of Easedale valley.

Look at Figures 12.11 and 12.22.

C5 A farmer in Easedale is thinking of using some of his land on the valley floor for a caravan site. Describe the advantages and disadvantages of this change of land use.

Core Discussion

LAND USE CONFLICT IN THE GREAT LANGDALE VALLEY

Imagine that the area inside the dashed line on the map shown in Figure 12.25 is to be developed. Three plans have been put forward for developing the site as:

(a) a forestry plantation
(b) a quarry
(c) a camping and caravan site

There are many arguments as to which is the best plan and the local residents have formed themselves into associations.

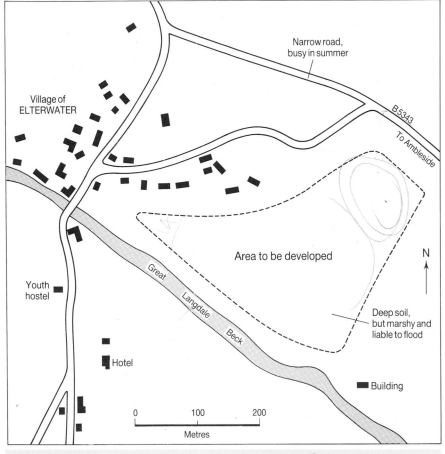

Figure 12.25 Area to be developed

Figure 12.26 The development site

Task 1 Work in groups of four. Each group represents a Local Residents' Association. Decide which person should be:
(a) in favour of the forestry plantation
(b) in favour of the quarry
(c) in favour of the camping and caravan site
(d) chairperson of the association

Task 2 The three people in favour of the different plans must discuss the advantages and disadvantages of each proposal. Some suggestions are given here but try to think of others.

The three people in favour of the different plans should each:
(a) write down the arguments for their plan and the arguments against the other plans
(b) read their arguments
(c) present their case to the rest of the group.

Task 3
(a) The chairperson listens to the arguments for the different plans and writes down the most important points.
(b) The chairperson decides which plan would be best for the local people.

Task 4 The chairperson reports to the rest of the class, giving reasons for the decision made.

Figure 12.27 A forestry plantation

ARGUMENTS FOR THE FORESTRY PLANTATION

- It will provide some jobs and there might eventually be a saw-mill.
- It will save Britain from importing trees.
- There will be facilities for tourists: a picnic site and a nature trail.
- It will shelter nearby farmland and houses.
- It will reduce soil erosion.
- It will reduce flooding of the Great Langdale Beck.

ARGUMENTS AGAINST THE FORESTRY PLANTATION

- Rows of alien trees spoil the landscape.
- It increases the risk of fire.
- There may be more foxes and rabbits, which will annoy nearby farmers.

ARGUMENTS FOR THE QUARRY

- It will provide a lot of permanent jobs.
- It will encourage people to stay in the area.
- People with jobs spend more money.
- It will employ lorry drivers.
- The rocks are needed so that new houses can be built out of local stone.

ARGUMENTS AGAINST THE QUARRY

- The noise and dust will upset local people, tourists and farmers.
- It will be an eyesore, which may reduce the number of tourists.
- There will be many heavy lorries on the road.

Figure 12.28 A quarry

ARGUMENTS FOR THE CAMPING AND CARAVAN SITE

- It will attract more tourists, who will spend money here.
- It will provide some jobs in the summertime.
- It will take tourists away from the overcrowded parts of the Lake District.

ARGUMENTS AGAINST THE CAMPING AND CARAVAN SITE

- Large numbers of tourists and their cars make a lot of noise.
- Tourists leave litter, which may be dangerous to animals.
- Tourists may trespass on nearby farms.
- Large numbers of tourists can wear away hillsides and the banks of rivers and lakes.
- The cars will cause congestion.

Figure 12.29 A camp and caravan site

UNIT ⑬

Landforms made by Melting Ice

Core Text

13A WHEN THE ICE MELTED

150 000 years ago ice-sheets covered most of Britain and Europe. Then, gradually, the climate became warmer. The ice in the south melted first. Then, as the temperatures continued to rise, the rest of the ice melted, leaving glaciers only in the highest mountains. There have been 20 of these Ice Ages in the last two million years. The last one ended only 10 000 years ago.

13B MORAINE

During the Ice Age the ice-sheets were over one kilometre thick in places. This made them very powerful and they eroded huge amounts of rock. The pieces of rock they picked up and carried are called **moraine**. There are different types of moraine.

Surface moraine is pieces of rock eroded from the hillside or fallen from the slopes above.

Ground moraine has been eroded from the rock underneath. It has been crushed into small pieces.

Terminal moraine is found at the front of a glacier or ice-sheet.

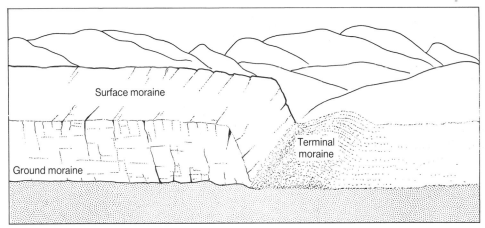

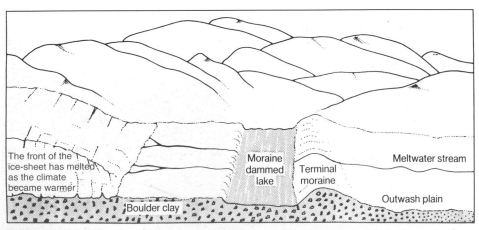

1. **At the coldest time in the Ice Age, this is the furthest the ice-sheet reached.**

2. **As the ice-sheet melts, it leaves behind deposits.**

Figure 13.1 Deposits left by ice-sheets

13C DEPOSITS LEFT BY ICE

When these enormous ice-sheets melted, they dropped all the moraine they were carrying. These deposits now make important landforms all over Europe. The main landforms and their uses are now described in more detail.

13D TERMINAL MORAINES

Terminal moraines were formed in the following way:
- the ice-sheet moved southwards to the point where the climate was warm enough for it to melt
- the ice bulldozed loose soil and rock in front of it
- all the moraine was dropped where the ice melted, building up small ridges
- these ridges of sand, gravel and boulders at the end of an ice-sheet or glacier are called **terminal moraines**
- terminal moraines are made of jagged pieces of rock and are unsorted (large and small pieces are mixed together).

Terminal moraines affect people in different ways:
- they make poor farmland as they have thin soils and little water near the surface
- they are often left as heath or covered with trees
- if they are not too steep, they provide dry land on which to build.

Figure 13.2 A boulder clay soil

13E BOULDER CLAY

Boulder clay is formed in the following way:
- ice carries moraine beneath and on top of it
- when the ice melts, it deposits the moraine
- this forms a covering of soil, called **boulder clay** or **till**
- this is a clay soil, with stones of different sizes in it.

Boulder clay affects people in different ways:
- the gentle slopes and fertile soil make it very useful for farming
- the gentle slopes are suitable for building on
- the land is sometimes waterlogged and difficult to plough.

13F MORAINE-DAMMED LAKES

Moraine-dammed lakes are formed in the following way:
- ice deposits a ridge of terminal moraine
- as the ice-sheet thaws, meltwater is trapped behind the terminal moraine
- a **moraine-dammed lake** builds up, which may drain away in time.

Moraine-dammed lakes affect people in different ways:
- they provide reservoirs for nearby towns
- they can be used for water sports
- they make it difficult to travel between places on either side.

Figure 13.3 A moraine-dammed lake in the Lake District

13G OUTWASH PLAINS

Outwash plains are formed in the following way:
- meltwater streams rush through the terminal moraine picking up rock pieces
- the streams then drop these pieces beyond the terminal moraine as they slow down
- the largest pieces are dropped first, for example gravel, followed by smaller ones, for example sand
- these areas of sand and gravel, rounded and sorted by meltwater, are called **outwash plains**.

Outwash plains affect people in different ways:
- their thin, stony soils make very poor farmland and so they are often left as heath and woodland
- they are sometimes marshy and difficult to build on
- the sand and gravel can be quarried for the building industry.

Figure 13.4 An outwash plain

13H AFTER THE ICE AGE

After the ice-sheets melted, the meltwater returned to the sea and the sea level rose. Some of our river valleys were drowned by the sea and became sea inlets. This is how fiords (see 12F) and estuaries formed in lowland Britain.

Then the land level began to rise because the enormous weight of ice had been lifted from it. In Scotland, the land has now risen many metres, and beaches, which were once washed by waves, are now well above sea level. These are called **raised beaches** and provide useful flat land in the upland areas of north-west Scotland.

Core Questions

Look at 13A.

1 When did the Ice Age end?

Look at 13B.

2 What is 'moraine'?

3 Name three different types of moraine.

Look at Figures 13.1 and 13.5.

4 Name landforms A to D in Figure 13.5, choosing from terminal moraine, outwash plain, boulder clay, moraine-dammed lake.

Look at 13D.

5 How does a terminal moraine form?

Look at 13F.

6 Explain how a moraine-dammed lake forms.

7 In what ways can a moraine-dammed lake be used?

Look at 13G.

8 What carries away moraine and builds-up outwash plains?

Look at 13E.

9 Which of the statements A to C on page 117 describes boulder clay?

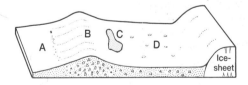

Figure 13.5 Glacial deposits

A

made up of clay, with large and small stones in it

B

made up of a mixture of boulders, pebbles and smaller rocks

C

made up of larger stones, separated from smaller ones

Look at 13G.

10 Which of the statements A to C above describes an outwash plain?

Look at 13H.

11 How are raised beaches formed?

F Questions

CASE STUDY OF EAST ANGLIA

Look at Figure 13.7.

F1 How many times was East Anglia covered with ice during the Ice Age?

Look at Figure 13.10.

F2 Which ice advance covered most of East Anglia?

Look at Figure 13.11.

F3 Which glacial deposit covers the largest area of East Anglia?

Look at Figure 13.8.

F4 Describe how East Anglia's boulder clay soils were formed.

Look at Figure 13.9.

F5 Describe how the Cromer Ridge formed.

Look at Figures 13.8 and 13.12.

F6 In what ways is boulder clay soil used?

Look at Figures 13.9 and 13.12.

F7 In what ways is terminal moraine used?

Look at Figures 13.12 and 13.13.

F8 Do you agree with the statement below? Give reasons for your answer.
'The outwash sands of East Anglia are of no use to anyone.'

G Questions

CASE STUDY OF EAST ANGLIA

Look at Figure 13.11.

G1 What are the most common glacial deposits in East Anglia?

Look at Figures 13.11 and 13.12.

G2 Describe the connection between the location of woodland in East Anglia and glacial deposits.

Look at Figure 13.13.

G3 Describe how the outwash plain of the Breckland was formed.

G4 Give one advantage and one disadvantage of the outwash plain to the people of East Anglia.

Look at Figure 13.9.

G5 Do you think the Cromer Ridge has been useful to the people of Norfolk? Give reasons for your answer.

Look at Figures 13.8 and 13.12.

G6 Do you agree with the statement below? Give reasons for your answer.
'The importance of cereal farming in East Anglia is entirely the result of its climate'

Figure 13.6 Barley growing on the fertile boulder clay soil of East Anglia

CASE STUDY OF EAST ANGLIA

Figure 13.7

Introduction

East Anglia is a lowland area in eastern England. It includes the counties of Norfolk and Suffolk, and the northern part of Essex. During the Ice Age, ice-sheets from the north and east covered this region four times. In between, the climate was quite mild, the ice melted and prehistoric people lived there. Every time the ice-sheets covered East Anglia they left behind deposits, which now cover 90% of the region.

The biggest settlements here are Norwich and Ipswich, but it is mostly a farming region, one of the most important in Britain. The way that people live here today owes much to the deposits left in the Ice Age.

Figure 13.8

Boulder Clay Soils

The first ice-sheet came from the east but only just touched East Anglia and left boulder clay in the north-east. The second time the ice-sheets covered East Anglia they reached as far south as where London is today. When the ice quickly melted it deposited all the moraine it was carrying. This formed boulder clay which is over 40 m deep in places. The boulder clay made flat or gently rolling land, on which it is easy to use farm machinery. The land is very fertile and well-drained so a variety of crops grow well here. The climate is warm so there is a long growing season for the crops. It is also dry and sunny, which helps crops to ripen. Barley and wheat are grown and cattle graze the pastures in the flood plains of rivers too wet to plough.

Figure 13.9

Terminal Moraine

The third time the ice-sheets reached East Anglia they melted in the north. As they melted they deposited all the moraine they had been carrying, which built up into a ridge of terminal moraine. Because the ice-sheet stopped here for a long time a lot of moraine was deposited, building up a ridge that is over 100 m high and 15 km long. This is called the Cromer Ridge. Some of the rocks in the ridge have been carried from Norway and Sweden. The ridge is not very steep but it is made of large particles that are too light and dry to be used for growing crops. It is therefore mostly wooded with some left as heathland.

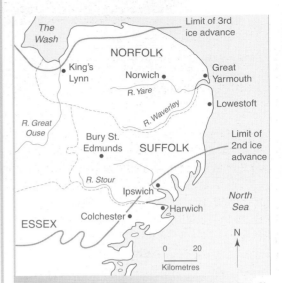

Figure 13.10 East Anglia

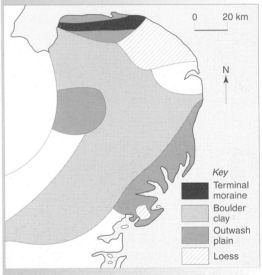

Figure 13.11 Glacial deposits of East Anglia (simplified)

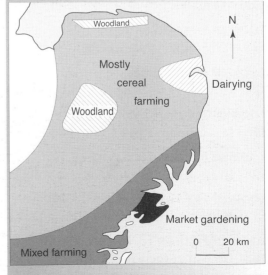

Figure 13.12 Land uses of East Anglia (simplified)

Figure 13.13

The Outwash Plains

Meltwater from the ice-sheet wriggled through the terminal moraine picking up some of the particles. It then flowed southwards, depositing the particles as it slowed down and lost energy. Finer sands and silts were carried further.

The outwash sands and gravels are quite dry and make a thin, acidic soil that is of little use for growing crops. Much of the outwash plains are covered with heath and, in the Breckland of Norfolk, a large area has been planted with coniferous trees. The Armed Forces also make use of this area. The sands and gravels have been quarried over the years for use in the building industry. Where these sands and gravels reach the coast in Suffolk they form cliffs. Because they are quite loose and soft they are eroded away quickly by waves. As they have been worn back, much land and several villages have disappeared into the sea, as well as the town of Dunwich, which at one time boasted two members of Parliament and 12 churches.

Figure 13.16 Cromer ridge of terminal moraine, north Norfolk

Figure 13.14

Eskers

As the ice-sheet began to melt, meltwater streams flowed under the ice, picking up and transporting much of the ground moraine the ice had eroded. These streams became so choked with moraine that they were forced to deposit much of it. Once all the meltwater had drained away, this deposited material was left as gravel ridges. These gravel ridges or eskers are found in north Norfolk and represent the beds of old meltwater streams.

Figure 13.15

Loess Deposits

The third time the ice reached this area, tiny particles of moraine were picked up by strong northerly winds and carried southwards over East Anglia. Here they were dropped and they now form the loess soils of south-east Essex.

Loess is particularly useful. It is very fertile and warms up quickly, making it ideal for growing fruit and vegetables. It is, however, prone to wind erosion if left bare of vegetation. The loess here goes under the name of 'brickearth' because in the nineteenth century it was used for making bricks throughout East Anglia.

Figure 13.17 Sand and gravel quarry, Norfolk

Extension Text

13J DRUMLINS

Drumlins are formed in the following way:
- melting ice deposits large amounts of moraine
- forward movement of the ice moulds the moraine to form streamlined mounds
- these small elliptical hills made of boulder clay, with a steeper upstream side, are called **drumlins**
- drumlins are often found in one area as 'swarms'
- water is sometimes trapped between drumlins, causing lakes or marsh to form.

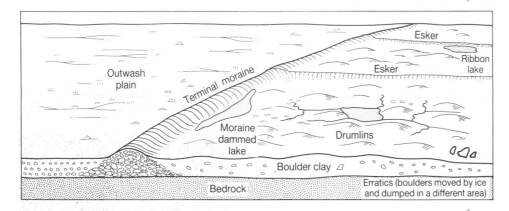

Figure 13.18 Glacial deposits

13K ESKERS

Eskers are formed in the following way:
- a meltwater stream flows in a tunnel beneath a melting ice-sheet
- the stream carries and deposits moraine, filling up the tunnel
- when all of the ice melts, a long ridge of moraine is left in the shape of the stream's tunnel
- these long ridges are called **eskers**.

13L LOESS

Loess is formed in the following way:
- the wind picks up tiny silt and clay particles of moraine
- the wind carries and deposits the particles beyond the ice-sheet
- these fine wind-blown deposits are called **loess** and make very fertile soils.

13M TYPES OF GLACIAL DEPOSITS

Carried by ice	Deposited by ice (glacial)	Deposited by meltwater (fluvio-glacial)	Deposited by wind
Lateral moraine (on the surface at the sides) Medial moraine (on the surface in the middle) Ground moraine	Boulder clay (or till) Drumlins Erratics Terminal moraine	Outwash plain Eskers	Loess

Glacial drift

E Questions

Read the Extension Text.

E1 What is (a) lateral moraine, (b) medial moraine, (c) glacial drift and (d) an erratic?

E2 Explain how the landform in Figure 13.19 has formed.

E3 Explain why eskers are long and narrow in appearance.

E4 Explain how loess forms.

C Questions

CASE STUDY OF EAST ANGLIA

Look at Figures 13.8, 13.9, 13.13, 13.14 and 13.15.

C1 Describe the glacial deposits left after each ice advance in East Anglia.

Look at Figure 13.14.

C2 Describe the formation of the eskers in north Norfolk.

Look at Figure 13.15.

C3 Describe how the loess in East Anglia has formed.

Look at Figures 13.8, 13.9, 13.13 and 13.14.

C4 Which have been of more benefit to the people of East Anglia: the glacial or the fluvio-glacial deposits?

Look at Figure 13.15.

C5 Describe the different points of view people might have towards the loess soils of East Anglia.

Figure 13.19

UNIT ⑭

Map Skills

Core Text

14A INTRODUCTION

Geographers study landscapes and try to work out why they look the way they do. A map is a view of a landscape from above, as you would see it from an aeroplane. Geographers make a lot of use of maps to get information about landscapes.

The **Ordnance Survey** (OS) is the organisation that produces the 'official' maps of Britain. Every Standard Grade Geography paper includes a map and it is nearly always an OS map.

For the Standard Grade examination, you need to be able to do the following:
1 use grid references to locate places
2 work out height and slope
3 work out distance using the scale
4 work out directions
5 draw and interpret cross-sections and transects
6 identify landforms made by rivers and ice
7 identify land uses in towns and the countryside.

14B SCALE AND DISTANCE

A map is much smaller than the landscape it shows. The scale of the map tells us how much smaller it is. It tells us by how much real distances and sizes have been reduced. Scale can be shown on a map as a **linear scale** or as a **representative fraction**. For example, a scale of 1:50 000 means that everything on the map is reduced to 1/50 000th of its real size.

To work out a distance, you use the scale of the map. Measure the distance on the map and then either use the linear scale or multiply by the representative fraction to find the real distance. If a map is of scale 1:50 000, any distance on the map has to be multiplied by 50 000 to find the real distance. For example, on a 1:50 000 map, 2 cm represents 1 km.

Figure 14.1 A linear scale representing 1:50 000.

14C DIRECTIONS

The vertical grid lines on an OS map point towards north (grid north). When giving directions, you should use the eight points of the compass, shown in Figure 14.2, and not words like 'top', 'bottom', 'left' and 'right'.

14D SYMBOLS

OS maps contain a wealth of information. There is not enough space for it all to be written on the map, so symbols are used. The symbols used on 1:50 000 maps are shown on the inside back cover of this book.

14E FOUR-FIGURE GRID REFERENCES

OS maps are divided into squares by blue grid lines running north–south and east–west. Places are located on OS maps using these grid lines.

A four-figure grid reference gives the location of a grid square. To work out a four-figure grid reference, for example square A in Figure 14.3:
• note the number of the vertical grid line to the west (left) of square A (45)
• note the number of the horizontal grid line south of (below) square A (86).

The four-figure grid reference of square A is 4586.

To find a four-figure grid reference, for example square 4786:
• find the point where the 47 vertical grid line meets the 86 horizontal grid line
• square 4786 is to the north-east of this point (up and to the right).

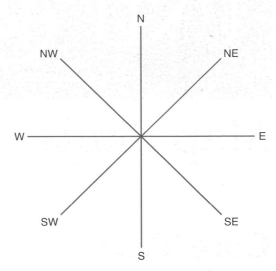

Figure 14.2 The eight points of the compass.

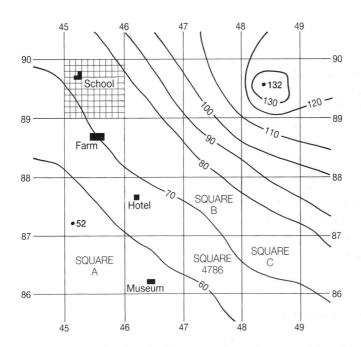

Figure 14.3 Working out four-figure grid references.

14F HEIGHT AND SLOPE

The height of the land is shown in two ways on OS maps:

1 **spot heights**, which are black dots, have the height in metres next to them

2 **contour lines**, which are brown lines, join places with the same height. On 1:50 000 maps contour lines are drawn 10 m apart, as shown in Figure 14.3.

Contour lines also show the slope of the land. If the contour lines are close together, the slope is steep. If they are far apart, the slope is gentle (see Figure 14.4).

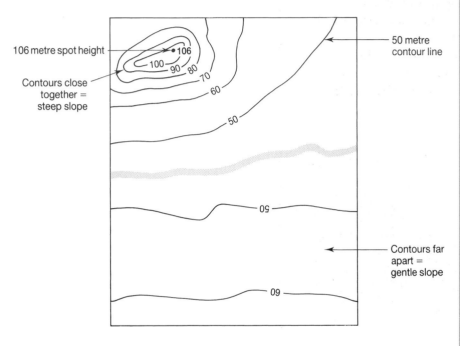

Figure 14.4 Contour lines and spot heights

F Questions

Look at the map of the Loch Kishorn area on the inside front cover of this book.

F1 What is the highest point in (a) square 8446 and (b) square 8538?

F2 Which square has the steeper slopes: 8345 or 8143?

F3 Why is the road going through square 8141 so twisty?

F4 Give two differences between the main river in square 8342 and the main river in square 8445.

F5 Find the car park in square 8443. Imagine you were walking from the car park south along the A896. Write down the order in which you would pass these features: viewpoint, Tornapress, post office, Courthill Ho.

F6 Match the descriptions below with the grid squares 8240, 8346 and 8047:

(a) steep mountains with a corrie and corrie loch

(b) gentle slopes and a shingle beach

(c) steep slopes with stream flowing south.

F7 Do you think the area shown on the map is popular with tourists? Give reasons for your answer.

G Questions

Look at the map of the Loch Kishorn area on the inside front cover of this book.

G1 Describe the characteristics of the River Kishorn in square 8342.

G2 Choosing from squares 8647, 8047 and 8546, which square contains (a) a corrie loch, (b) a lake in an overdeepened hollow and (c) a shallow lake, probably moraine-dammed?

G3 Which of the following grid squares contains a corrie: 8144, 8642 or 8242? Give reasons for your answer.

G4 Figure 14.5 is a cross-section along the 41 line on the map. Which of the letters A to D shows the position of (a) the River Kishorn, (b) coniferous woodland, (c) the A896 and (d) a waterfall?

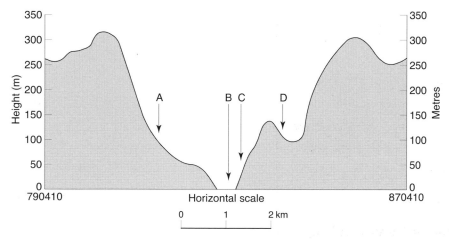

Figure 14.5 Cross section from 790410 to 870410

G5 Suggest why there is so little forestry in the map area.

G6 Do you think the area shown on the map is popular with tourists? Give reasons for your answer.

Extension Text

14G SIX-FIGURE GRID REFERENCES

Four-figure grid references locate grid squares. To locate exact points, six-figure grid references are needed.

To work out a six-figure grid reference, for example for the school in Figure 14.3, imagine that square 4589 is divided into 100 smaller squares. The school is two small squares east of the 45 easting and seven small squares north of the 89 northing. The six-figure grid reference of the school is 452897.

14H DRAWING A CROSS-SECTION

A cross-section is a side view of the landscape. It shows the exact shape of the physical landscape. You can draw a cross-section in the following way:

- place a strip of paper over the line of your section and mark where each contour crosses the edge of the paper
- write down the height of each contour next to its mark and also write down the names of other features, for example rivers
- draw a graph with a horizontal axis the same length as the line of your section
- choose a suitable vertical scale for the graph
- place the paper below the graph and draw pencil lines from each contour mark to the correct height on the graph (see Figure 14.6)
- join the points at the top of each line to produce the cross-section and rub out the pencil lines
- write the names of the other features on your section
- underneath the two axes, write the grid reference of your starting point and finishing point
- give the cross-section a title.

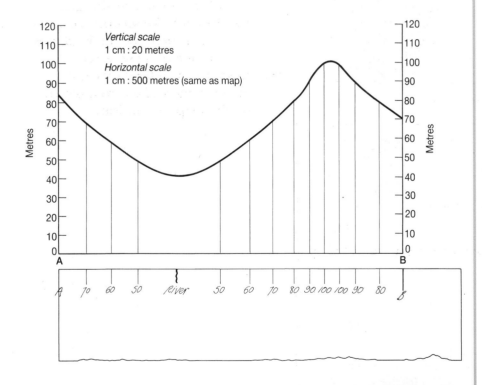

Figure 14.6 A cross section

14J DRAWING A TRANSECT

A transect is a line along which the locations of features of the human or physical landscape are noted. On a map, a transect is used to show the land uses along a line and, in particular, to show the relationship between relief and land uses. You can draw a transect in the following way:

- select a suitable transect line on the map that will clearly show differences in land use and relief
- draw a cross-section, as described in 14H
- underneath the section draw several rows, one for each of the main land uses (see Figure 14.7)
- along each row, record the locations of the different land uses, as shown in figure 14.7.

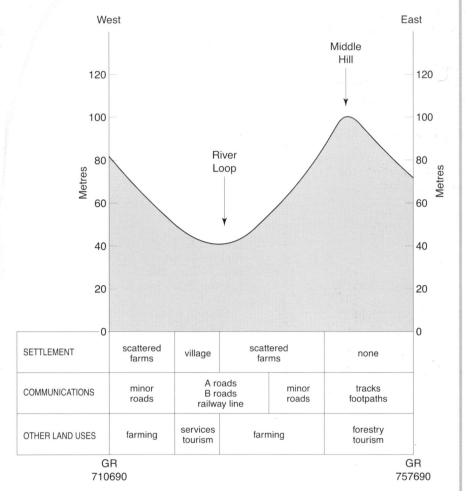

SETTLEMENT	scattered farms	village	scattered farms		none
COMMUNICATIONS	minor roads	A roads B roads railway line		minor roads	tracks footpaths
OTHER LAND USES	farming	services tourism	farming		forestry tourism

GR
710690

GR
757690

Figure 14.7 A transect across the Loop Valley

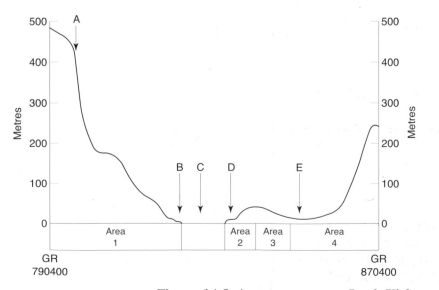

GR
790400

GR
870400

Figure 14.8 A transect across Loch Kishorn

ⒸQuestions

Look at the map of the Loch Kishorn area on the inside front cover of this book.

C1 Describe the changes along the River Kishorn and its valley from where it rises at 838479 to its mouth at 835423.

C2 What evidence is there that the area shown on the map has been glaciated?

C3 Draw a cross-section along the 43 northing from 800430 to 850430.

C4 The cross-section in Figure 14.8 has been drawn along the 40 northing.

  (a) Match letters A to E on the cross-section with the following landforms: raised beach, crags, fiord, flood-plain, corrie and shingle.

  (b) Beneath the section are areas 1 to 4. Describe the land uses in each of these areas.

C5 Describe the advantages and disadvantages of the area shown on the map for tourism.

INDEX